English

Assessment Papers

9–10 years

Book 2

OXFORD

UNIVERSITY PRESS

OXFORD
UNIVERSITY PRESS

Great Clarendon Street, Oxford, OX2 6DP, United Kingdom

Oxford University Press is a department of the University of Oxford.
It furthers the University's objective of excellence in research, scholarship,
and education by publishing worldwide. Oxford is a registered trade mark of
Oxford University Press in the UK and in certain other countries

British Library Cataloguing in Publication Data
Data available

978-0-19-274004-5

10 9 8 7 6 5

Paper used in the production of this book is a natural, recyclable
product made from wood grown in sustainable forests.
The manufacturing process conforms to the environmental
regulations of the country of origin.

Printed in China

Acknowledgements

The publishers would like to thank the following for permissions to
use copyright material:

Page make-up: OKS Prepress, India
Illustrations: Lisa Smith (Sylvie Poggio Artists Agency)
Cover illustrations: Lo Cole

P2 'You Can't Be That' from *Thawing Frozen Frogs* by Brian Patten, copyright
© Brian Patten, 1990. Reproduced by permission of the author; p7 extract
from *A Pack of Liars* by Anne Fine, copyright © Anne Fine, 1988. Published by
Penguin Ltd, reprinted by permission of David Higham Associates; p12 extract
from *How to run a marathon*, by Cathy Shipton and Liz McColgan copyright
© Cathy Shipton and Liz McColgan 1997. Reprinted by permission of
HarperCollins Publishers Ltd; p23 extract from *Questions and Answers: Oceans
and Rivers* by Barbara Taylor © Kingfisher Publications Plc 2000. Reproduced
by permission of the publisher, all rights reserved; p29 extract from
War Horse by Michael Morpurgo, copyright © 1990 Michael Morpurgo.
Published by Egmont UK Ltd London and used with permission; p41 extract
from *Plan UK* leaflet; reproduced by permission of Plan UK; p46 extract from
The Voyage of the Dawn Treader by C S Lewis copyright © C S Lewis Pte Ltd 1952.
Extract reprinted by permission; pp52–53 extract from *Wordly Wise* by Barrie
Wade, Ann Wade and Maggie Moore, Storychest 1986; p58 extract from
'Polar explorer brought in from the cold after 38 years' by Esther Adley,
17 October 2006. Copyright © Guardian News and Media Limited 2007.

Although we have made every effort to trace and contact all
copyright holders before publication this has not been possible in all
cases. If notified, the publisher will rectify any errors or omissions at
the earliest opportunity.

Links to third party websites are provided by Oxford in good faith
and for information only. Oxford disclaims any responsibility for
the materials contained in any third party website referenced in
this work.

Before you get started

What is Bond?

This book is part of the Bond Assessment Papers series for English, which provides **thorough and continuous practice of key English skills** from ages five to thirteen. Bond's English resources are ideal preparation for Key Stage 1 and Key Stage 2 SATs, the 11+ and other selective school entrance exams.

What does this book cover and how can it be used to prepare for exams?

English 9–10 years Book 1 and *Book 2* can be used both for general practice and as part of the run up to 11+ exams, Key Stage 2 SATs and other selective exams. The papers practise comprehension, spelling, grammar and vocabulary work. The coverage is also matched to the National Curriculum and the National Literacy Strategy. It is outside the scope of this book to practise extended and creative writing skills. *Bond Focus on Writing* provides full coverage of writing skills.

What does the book contain?

- **12 papers** – each one contains 100 questions.

- **Tutorial links throughout** – – this icon appears in the margin next to the questions. It indicates links to the relevant section in *How to do 11+ English*, our invaluable subject guide that offers explanations and practice for all core question types.

- **Scoring devices** – there are score boxes in the margins and a Progress Chart on page 68. The chart is a visual and motivating way for children to see how they are doing. It also turns the score into a percentage that can help decide what to do next.

- **Next Steps Planner** – advice on what to do after finishing the papers can be found on the inside back cover.

- **Answers** – located in an easily-removed central pull-out section.

How can you use this book?

One of the great strengths of Bond Assessment Papers is their flexibility. They can be used at home, in school and by tutors to:

- set **timed formal practice** tests – allow about 45 minutes per paper. Reduce the suggested time limit by five minutes to practise working at speed.

- provide **bite-sized chunks** for regular practice
- **highlight strengths and weaknesses** in the core skills
- identify **individual needs**
- set **homework**
- follow a **complete 11+ preparation strategy** alongside *The Parents' Guide to the 11+* (see below).

It is best to start at the beginning and work though the papers in order. If you are using the book as part of a careful run-in to the 11+, we suggest that you also have four other essential Bond resources close at hand:

How to do 11+ English: the subject guide that explains all the question types practised in this book. Use the cross-reference icons to find the relevant sections.

Focus on Comprehension: the practical handbook that clearly shows children how to read and understand the text, understand the questions and assess their own answers.

Focus on Writing: the essential resource that explains the key components of successful writing.

The Parents' Guide to the 11+: the step-by-step guide to the whole 11+ experience. It clearly explains the 11+ process, provides guidance on how to assess children, helps you to set complete action plans for practice and explains how you can use *English 9–10 years Book 1* and *Book 2* as part of a strategic run-in to the exam.

See the inside front cover for more details of these books.

What does a score mean and how can it be improved?

It is unfortunately impossible to predict how a child will perform when it comes to the 11+ (or similar) exam if they achieve a certain score on any practice book or paper. Success on the day depends on a host of factors, including the scores of the other children sitting the test. However, we can give some guidance on what a score indicates and how to improve it.

If children colour in the Progress Chart on page 68, this will give an idea of present performance in percentage terms. The Next Steps Planner inside the back cover will help you to decide what to do next to help a child progress. It is always valuable to go over wrong answers with children. If they are having trouble with any particular question type, follow the tutorial links to *How to do 11+ English* for step-by-step explanations and further practice.

Don't forget the website...!

Visit www.bond11plus.co.uk for lots of advice, information and suggestions on everything to do with Bond, the 11+ and helping children to do their best.

Key words

Some special words are used in this book. You will find them in **bold** each time they appear in the Papers. These words are explained here.

abbreviation	a word or words which are shortened
abstract noun	a word referring to a concept or idea *love*
acronym	a word or letter string made up from the initial letters of other words
adjectival phrase	a group of words describing a noun
adjective	a word that describes somebody or something
adverb	a word that gives extra meaning to a verb
alphabetical order	words arranged in the order found in the alphabet
antonym	a word with a meaning opposite to another word *hot – cold*
clause	a section of a sentence with a verb
collective noun	a word referring to a group *swarm*
compound word	a word made up of two other words *football*
conjunction	a word used to link sentences, phrases or words *and, but*
connective	a word or words that join clauses or sentences
contraction	two words shortened into one with an apostrophe placed where the letter/s have been dropped *do not = don't*
definition	a meaning of a word
dialect	regional variation of vocabulary in the spoken language
diminutive	a word implying smallness *booklet*
future tense	form of a verb showing something that will or may happen
homophone	a word that has the same sound as another but a different meaning or spelling *right/write*
metaphor	an expression in which something is described in terms usually associated with another *the sky is a <u>sapphire</u> sea*
modal verb	a verb that changes the meaning of other verbs, for example can, will
noun	a word for somebody or something
onomatopoeic	a word that echoes a sound associated with its meaning *hiss*
parenthesis	this is a word or phrase that is separated off from the main sentence by brackets, commas or dashes usually because it contains additional information not essential to its understanding
past tense	form of a verb showing something that has already happened
personal pronoun	a pronoun used when writing about ourselves *I, you*
phrase	a group of words that act as a unit
plural	more than one *cats*
possessive pronoun	a pronoun showing to whom something belongs *mine, ours, his, hers, yours, theirs*
prefix	a group of letters added to the beginning of a word *un, dis*
preposition	a word that relates other words to each other – *he sat <u>behind</u> me, the book <u>on</u> the table*
present tense	form of a verb showing something happening now
pronoun	a word used to replace a noun
relative clause	a special type of clause that makes the meaning of a noun more specific, for example The prize *that I won* was a book
proper noun	the names of people, places etc. *Ben*
reported speech	what has been said, without using the exact words or speech marks
root word	a word to which prefixes or suffixes can be added to make another word *<u>quick</u>ly*
singular	one *cat*
suffix	a group of letters added to the end of a word *ly, ful*
synonym	a word with the same or very similar meaning to another word *quick – fast*
verb	a 'doing' or 'being' word

You Can't Be That

I told them:
When I grow up
I'm not going to be a scientist
Or someone who reads the news on TV.
No, a million birds will fly through me.   5
I'M GOING TO BE A TREE!

They said,
You can't be that. No, you can't be that.

I told them:
When I grow up   10
I'm not going to be an airline pilot,
A dancer, a lawyer or an MC.
No, huge whales will swim in me.
I'M GOING TO BE AN OCEAN!

They said,   15
You can't be that. No, you can't be that.

I told them:
I'm not going to be a DJ,
A computer programmer, a musician or beautician.
No, streams will flow through me,   20
I'll be the home of eagles;
I'll be full of nooks, crannies, valleys and fountains.
I'M GOING TO BE A RANGE OF MOUNTAINS!

They said,
You can't be that. No, you can't be that.   25

I asked them:
Just what do you think I am?
Just a child, they said,
And children always become
At least one of the things   30
We want them to be.

They do not understand me.
I'll be a stable if I want, smelling of fresh hay,
I'll be a lost glade in which unicorns still play.
They do not realise I can fulfil any ambition.   35
They do not realise among them
Walks a magician.

Brian Patten

Underline the correct answers.

1 The child wanted to be the home of eagles. What was he going to be?

(a tree, an ocean, a range of mountains)

2 What does the child ultimately want to be?

(a lawyer, a beautician, a magician)

Answer these questions.

3 Find a word in the poem that rhymes with 'tree'. _____

4 Who do you think 'they' (line 7) could be?

_____

5 How does the text indicate when adults are talking?

_____

6–8 Read lines 26–31 again. What impression is given of these adults?
How do you think the child might feel?

_____

_____

_____

_____

9–10 Describe the child's character using evidence from the poem.

_____

_____

_____

_____

Write the **plural** form of each of these **nouns**.

11 lantern _____   **12** atlas _____

13 disease _____   **14** chocolate _____

15 calf _____   **16** athlete _____

17 fox _____   **18** roof _____

Add a **verb** to complete these sentences. Each verb may be used only once.

D 6

read   searched   ran   went   grew   felt

19 Marcus _____ for the bus.

20 Meena _____ the Internet for information on the Moon.

21 The teacher _____ the chapter to the class.

22 The flowers _____ quickly in the greenhouse.

23 Mr Robson _____ closer to the strange shape.

24 The fire-fighters _____ the force of the explosion.

6

D 5

Add the missing punctuation at the end of each sentence.

25 You should always wear a helmet when riding your bike ___

26 The snake slipped silently through the fallen leaves ___

27 Quick, we've got to go ___

28 Have you done your homework tonight ___

29 Hurry, before it starts to rain ___

30 What is hiding in the mess under your bed ___

31 Queen Victoria served her country for many years ___

7

E 2

Write a word with the same letter string and same sound as each of these words.

32 dove	_____	33 borough	_____
34 fought	_____	35 bough	_____
36 though	_____	37 move	_____
38 mellow	_____	39 rough	_____

8

D 9

Underline one word in each group which is not a **synonym** for the rest.

40 fast	quick	rapid	slow	speedy
41 display	hide	exhibit	demonstrate	reveal
42 guzzle	slurp	quaff	sip	gulp
43 gregarious	lonesome	isolated	remote	solitary
44 angry	sulky	cranky	furious	content

| 45 misleading | false | accurate | fake | untrue |
| 46 endanger | safeguard | defend | protect | look after |

Underline the **pronouns** in the following passage.

47–54 We regretted leaving our jumpers behind. It had become cold and we could have done with them for protection from the biting wind. Still we battled on against the elements. It was so important we made it before darkness fell.

Underline the silent letter in each of these words.

55 answer	_____	56 ballet	_____
57 honour	_____	58 wriggle	_____
59 solemn	_____	60 rhythm	_____
61 island	_____	62 exhibit	_____

Copy each of these **phrases** making each **noun plural**. Don't forget to add the missing apostrophe.

63–64 the two car horn _____

65–66 the five girl jumper _____

67–68 the six bird beak _____

69–70 the four dog lead _____

Add a **suffix** to each of these words.

71 resource _____

72 shape _____

73 excite _____

74 woe _____

75 remote _____

76 false _____

77 tame _____

Choose an **adverb** to fill each gap. Each **adverb** may be used only once.

cheekily   wearily   lovingly   accidentally   wistfully   angrily   tunefully

78 Alice sang _____.

79 Nina gently and _____ washed and set her Gran's hair.

80 Manjit tripped and _____ dropped the paint pot.

81 Jacob sighed _____ as he looked at the brand new sports car.

82 Sam _____ climbed into bed.

83 Tuhil yelled _____ at his dog as he chased a cat.

84 Anne _____ chuckled.

7

Rewrite these sentences changing them from **plural** to **singular**.

85–86 The teams played their best.

_____

87–89 The cinemas in the area were showing the latest releases.

_____

90–92 The bonfires burnt for many hours.

_____

8

Copy the **proper nouns**, adding the missing capital letters.

93–100

february	bath rugby club	aberdeen
sydney harbour	gangster	windsor castle
contest	outcome	blue peter
ben nevis	combination	alex roberts

_____   _____

_____   _____

_____   _____

_____   _____

8

Now go to the Progress Chart to record your score!   Total   100

It was not until the first week in November that replies from the Sticklebury penpals began to trickle into class. Oliver's letter from Simon was first to arrive.

Dear Oliver Boot,

You shouldn't have said in your letter that I might never grow out of my horrible habits because my mother read that bit by mistake, and my father had to give her a whisky to stop her crying. [5]

How are you? I am very well. I have been sent to the ~~psi psyich pchi pci~~ psychologist because of the worse things that were private. So they aren't quite so private any more.

I tell terrible lies. It drives them mad, but I can't help it. I also run away from school. Quite often. But then I did them both at the same time, and that was a mistake. I ran away [10] from school after morning assembly, and my next door neighbour pounced on me while I was half in and half out of the downstairs lavatory window, sneaking back in our house. I told her the school nurse sent me home because I had headlice, which was the only thing I could think of. But that evening the next door neighbour told Mum that I mustn't come round and play with her little Peter any more till I'd been sorted out. And Mum said: Sorted Out About [15] What? And she said: About Headlice, Of Course. And then my mum went up the wall.

I begged her not to, with real tears in my eyes, but she wrote to the school nurse anyway, demanding an explanation and an apology. But I just happened to lose the letter inside a dustbin as I walked past it. I needn't have bothered, because Mum was so angry she phoned the school anyway. And when my teacher said: Simon, Where [20] Is The Letter From Your Mother? I just panicked and told her my mother wasn't really my mother at all because I am a long lost, secret son of the Prince, and my mum and dad just pretend I am theirs to save the Queen from unbearable embarrassment.

So then my teacher said: Oh Yes? all sarcastically. And I panicked some more and said I could prove it with my handwriting. It is this bad because I am by nature [25] left-handed, I said, and I am forced to write with my right hand to keep up my disguise.

All Right, my teacher said. Here Is A Pen, Simon. Write With Your Left Hand. So I asked: What Shall I Write? and she said tartly: How About This Is A Shocking Pack Of Lies? So I wrote with my left hand, and it was even worse than this, if you can imagine. And when I said it was simply because I hadn't had enough practice writing [30] with my left hand, my teacher went right up the wall.

How are you? I hope you are quite well.
Yours sincerely,
Simon Huggett

From A Pack of Liars by Anne Fine

Underline the correct answers.

1 (Simon's, Oliver's, Peter's) letter was first to arrive.

2 Simon thinks he was sent to the psychologist because (he tells lies, he runs away from school, he has headlice).

3 Simon (did, didn't) have headlice.

Answer these questions.

4 What is meant by the line 'replies from the Sticklebury penpals began to trickle into class' (lines 1–2)?

_____

_____

_____

5 What does Simon mean when he says 'And then my mum went up the wall' (line 16)?

_____

_____

6 Why do you think Simon highlights the fact that he had 'real' tears (line 17)?

_____

_____

_____

7–8 In lines 18–19 Simon says 'But I just happened to lose the letter inside a dustbin as I walked past it.' What did Simon really do with the letter and why do you think he phrased it the way he did?

_____

_____

_____

9–10 Do you think Simon's left-handed argument is a valid one? What does it tell us about Simon's character?

_____

_____

_____

_____

Circle the words that either are or can be **nouns**.

D 6

11–17 herd   cheese   playful   booklet

         under   Richard   antelope   fracture

         hate   secure   questioned   similar

7

Add one of the **prefixes** to each word to make its **antonym**.

D 9
E 2

      non   im   ir   dis

18 _____responsible

19 _____existent

20 _____approve

21 _____balance

22 _____relevant

23 _____possible

24 _____charge

25 _____similar

8

Add the missing commas to these sentences.

D 4

26–27 Jess had to feed her cat give fresh water to the chickens take the dog for a walk and let the sheep out before school.

28–30 It was wet blustery sunny warm and windy during the Todd family walk.

31–33 Joseph spent his pocket money on a small pot of paint for his model aircraft a magazine a card for his mum's birthday a chocolate bar and a drink.

8

Write two **antonyms** for each of these words.

D 9

34–35 laugh   _____   _____

36–37 violent   _____   _____

38–39 small   _____   _____

6

Underline one **clause** (a section of a sentence with a **verb**) in each of these sentences.

D 2

40 Aimee wanted to go horse riding despite the pouring rain.

41 Nazar lost his coat at school on the coldest day of the year.

42 The snow fell heavily for many hours.

43 Dad stopped at the side of the road to answer his phone.

44 Helen ordered a cup of tea and an iced bun from the café on the high street.

45 Eleni worked hard at solving her maths problem despite her headache.

6

Add the **prefix** *sub* or *tele* to each of these words.

46 _____plot

47 _____standard

48 _____communications

49 _____normal

50 _____phone

51 _____merge

52 _____title

53 _____conscious

Write a more powerful **verb** for each of these verbs.

54 run _____

55 laugh _____

56 throw _____

57 swallow _____

58 wet _____

59 speak _____

Underline the **root word** for each of these words.

60 transatlantic

61 idleness

62 partnership

63 placement

64 non-toxic

65 unreal

66 dangerously

67 assessment

68 bicycle

Copy these sentences and write a **possessive pronoun** in place of the words in bold.

69–70 The apples on their side of the fence are **their apples** but those on our side are **our apples**.

_____

_____

71–72 **Your coat** is the same as **my coat**.

_____

73–74 **Kyle's bike** is bigger than **my bike**.

_____

75–76 **Jake's drink** tasted better than **Sarah's drink**.

_____

Add these **suffixes** to each word.

77 plan + ed = _____   **78** admit + ing = _____

79 ballot + ed = _____   **80** tax + ing = _____

81 refer + ed = _____   **82** cancel + ed = _____

83 test + ed = _____   **84** focus + ing = _____

85 prefer + ed = _____   **86** hop + ing = _____

○ 10

Add a different imperative **verb** to each of these sentences.

87 _____, there's a car coming!

88 _____, or we will be late.

89 _____, they're after us.

90 _____, in the name of the law!

91 _____ if you can't hear me at the back of the room.

92 _____ your percussion instruments.

93 _____ if you're happy!

○ 7

Add *ant*, *ance*, *ent* or *ence* to complete these words.

94–95 assist _____ assist _____

96–97 toler _____ toler _____

98–99 innoc _____ innoc _____

100 obedi _____

○ 7

Now go to the Progress Chart to record your score! Total ○ 100

Preparation for a marathon takes many months but at last it is **The Big Day**.

Depending on the time of the race, make sure you eat a small meal high in
carbohydrate at least three hours beforehand. You may feel too nervous to eat, but
you do need to top up your liver glycogen. Glycogen can only be stored in the liver
for about 12 hours and is a necessary source of energy in the latter stages of the run. 5

If you are staying away from home the night before the race, take a selection of
the breakfast you would usually eat with you as it's best not to introduce anything
different at this late stage. Don't be persuaded to alter your habits, no matter how
well-meaning your host may be.

Having worked out your route to the race, set out with plenty of time, aiming to get 10
there at least an hour before the start. Although you may find there is a very exciting
atmosphere, try not to let it deflect you from your preparation. You can find yourself stopping
and having chats and suddenly 20 minutes have gone by and you're not ready.

If you are with a club, they may supply transport and a safe place to store your kit,
otherwise the organisers of the event will offer secure storage. Strip down to your 15
running kit, apply the plasters, store your kit then … queue for the loo! This is a crucial
activity and at some events can take up to half an hour!

Cover up before the race with an old sweat-top or black bin-bag so as to keep
warm. You can discard it when you get going.

Keep a small bottle of water with you, sipping from time to time, until about 20 minutes 20
before the start. You will be supplied with water on all races and some events will give you
squash or a brand name replacement drink. Only use these if you are used to them in
training, as they can upset your stomach. Some runners use energy bars and dried fruit to
sustain their energy through the run; again, don't eat through the race if you're not used to it.

Set your own watch as you go over the start line, as it can be up to 10 minutes 25
after the actual start gun, depending on the attendance at the race. That way you can
monitor your own race.

Aim to run the first five miles at your predicted race speed. Being suddenly
surrounded by a variety of runners can throw you off, so run your own race and
don't worry about the rest. 30

You're off …
Enjoy the race!

From *Marathon Manual* by Cathy Shipton with Liz McColgan

Underline the correct answers.

1 You should finally eat (just before, three hours before, twelve hours before) the start of the race.

2 Why is it important to top up your glycogen levels before the race?

(it stops you feeling nervous, it tops up your energy levels, it allows you to skip breakfast)

3 Why can it sometimes take many minutes from the start of the race for the runner to actually cross the start line?

(because the runner isn't prepared, because there are many runners wanting to cross the start line, because some runners like to start the race by walking)

3

Answer these questions.

4 Why might the runner stay away from home the night before a race?

_____

5–6 Give two reasons why it is important to arrive approximately an hour before the race starts.

_____

_____

_____

7 Why does the author describe going to the loo as a 'crucial activity' (lines 16–17)?

_____

_____

8 What is the meaning of the word 'sustain' on line 24?

_____

9–10 Give two reasons why the use of a bin-bag or sweat-top is suggested.

_____

_____

_____

7

Add the missing *ie* or *ei* letters to complete each word correctly.

11 h_____r

12 dec_____ve

13 fr_____ght

14 v_____w

15 conc_____ve

16 y_____ld

17 n_____ghbours

18 s_____ze

19 conc_____ted

E 2

9

D 6

Rewrite each sentence as if you are writing about yourself.

20 She enjoys swimming.   _____

21 They made their favourite cakes.   _____

22 He loves playing football.   _____

23 The teacher stopped her on the way to class.

_____

4

D 9

Write an **antonym** for each of these words.

24 high   _____

25 cold   _____

26 over   _____

27 legal   _____

28 difficult   _____

29 mobile   _____

30 bought   _____

31 receive   _____

32 whisper   _____

9

Change the degree of possibility in these sentences by adding a different modal verb to each one, for example The children shall walk home from school.

33 The children _____ walk home from school.

34 The children _____ walk home from school.

35 The children _____ walk home from school.

36 The children _____ walk home from school.

37 The children _____ walk home from school.

D 6

5

Add the missing commas to these sentences.

D 4

38 Fed up because the computer continually broke down they decided to buy a new one.

39 The sunbathers lay on the beach all afternoon unaware of how burnt they were becoming.

40–41 The stranger a well-dressed man joined the party.

42 In Madagascar the inner skins of leaves are peeled and then stretched out in the tropical sun which dries and bleaches them.

43 While Henry was swimming at his local pool the lights suddenly went off.

44 When it was announced that the fancy-dress competition was about to take place we huddled together to plan our escape.

7

E 2

Write each of these words in its **plural** form.

45 punch	_____	**46** bus	_____
47 sausage	_____	**48** convoy	_____
49 dress	_____	**50** waltz	_____
51 tariff	_____	**52** thief	_____

8

D 6

Underline the **nouns** in this poem.

53–60 Daisy, Daisy,

Give me your answer do,

I'm half crazy

All for the love of you;

It won't be a stylish marriage,

For I can't afford a carriage –

But you'll look sweet

Upon the seat

Of a bicycle made for two!

Anon.

8

D 5

Rewrite these sentences and add the missing speech marks.

61–64 What do we do now? grumbled Jay through gritted teeth. They're bound to sabotage our camp.

They can't do anything until it gets dark, consoled Mimi. We'll just have to make sure we stay up all through the night.

_____

_____

_____

_____

65–68 I'm frozen, complained Jay. It really is cold and dark, he sighed. Maybe they aren't going to come back tonight.

Mimi considered Jay's comment. But maybe they will! she replied.

_____

_____

_____

_____

8

E 2

Write one word for each **definition**. Each word begins with '*g*'.

69 A hard, transparent substance that is easily broken. _____

70 A Roman man who was forced to fight for public amusement. _____

71 A movement that conveys a meaning. _____

72 A sphere showing the map of the world. _____

73 A valuable, yellow metal. _____

74 A small, flying insect that can bite people. _____

75 A slope. _____

76 Another name for rubbish. _____

8

E 2

Underline the correct **homophone** in each bracket.

77–78 The (boy, buoy) untied his boat from the (boy, buoy).

79–80 The (fair, fare) for a ride at the (fair, fare) was £3.00.

81–82 Jason (new, knew) his (new, knew) jeans would fit perfectly.

83–84 'Are you (sure/shore) we can see the (sure/shore) from here?' asked the children.

85–86 The (ewe, yew) died after eating the (ewe, yew), a very poisonous plant.

10

D 12

Underline the **reported speech** sentences only and write them again as direct speech.

87–94 Kate's dad called to her to hurry up.

'What's the time?' the teacher asked.

'Let's go to the playground,' pleaded the twins.

Sarah explained to Pete she was going on holiday soon.

The Singh family yelled to the passing boat that they needed help.

'Quick! The match starts in 10 minutes,' called Joel.

Mum asked her friend if she thought it might rain today.

'Have you found a snail yet?' queried Aimee.

_____

_____

_____

_____

8

D 8

Write the **diminutive** for each of these.

95 pig   _____   96 book   _____

97 duck   _____   98 hill   _____

99 owl   _____   100 statue   _____

6

Now go to the Progress Chart to record your score!   Total   100

Paper 4

'This is Lord Fauntleroy, Mrs Mellon,' he said. 'Lord Fauntleroy, this is Mrs Mellon, who is the housekeeper.'

    Cedric gave her his hand, his eyes lighting up.

    'Was it you who sent the cat?' he said. 'I'm much obliged to you ma'am.'

    Mrs Mellon's handsome old face looked as pleased as the face of the lodge-keeper's   5
wife had done.

    'I should know his lordship anywhere,' she said to Mr Havisham. 'He has the Captain's face and way. It's a great day, this, sir.'

    Cedric wondered why it was a great day. He looked at Mrs Mellon curiously. It
seemed to him for a moment as if there were tears in her eyes, and yet it was   10
evident she was not unhappy. She smiled down at him.

    'The cat left two beautiful kittens here,' she said. 'They shall be sent up to your
lordship's nursery.'

    Mr Havisham said a few words to her in a low voice.

    'In the library, sir,' Mrs Mellon replied. 'His lordship is to be taken there alone.'   15

    A few minutes later the very tall footman in livery, who had escorted Cedric to
the library door, opened it and announced: 'Lord Fauntleroy, my lord,' in quite a
majestic tone. If he was only a footman, he felt it was rather a grand occasion when
the heir came home to his own land and possessions, and was ushered into the
presence of the old Earl, whose place and title he was to take.   20

17

Cedric crossed the threshold into the room. It was a very large and splendid room, with massive carven furniture in it, and shelves upon shelves of books … For a moment Cedric thought there was nobody in the room, but soon he saw that by the fire burning on the wide hearth there was a large easy chair, and that in that chair someone was sitting – someone who did not at first turn to look at him.   25

But he had attracted attention in one quarter at least. On the floor, by the armchair, lay a dog, a huge tawny mastiff with body and limbs almost as big as a lion's; and this great creature rose majestically and slowly, and marched towards the little fellow with a heavy step.

Then the person in the chair spoke. 'Dougal,' he called, 'come back, sir.' …   30

Cedric put his hand on the big dog's collar in the most natural way in the world, and they strayed forward together, Dougal sniffing as he went.

And then the Earl looked up …

… Cedric looked at him just as he had looked at the woman at the lodge and at the housekeeper, and came quite close to him.   35

'Are you the Earl?' he said. 'I'm your grandson, you know, that Mr Havisham brought. I'm Lord Fauntleroy.'

He held out his hand because he thought it must be the polite and proper thing to do even with earls. 'I hope you are very well,' he continued, with the utmost friendliness. 'I'm very glad to see you.'   40

The Earl shook hands with him, with a curious gleam in his eyes; just at first he was so astonished that he scarcely knew what to say. He stared at the picturesque little apparition from under his shaggy brows, and took it all in from head to foot.

'Glad to see me, are you?' he said.

From *Little Lord Fauntleroy* by Frances Hodgson Burnett

Underline the correct answers.

1 Lord Fauntleroy's first name is (Mr Havisham, Dougal, Cedric).

2 Mrs Mellon had tears in her eyes because she (had dust in them, was sad, was happy).

3 On line 43 the Earl is described as having 'shaggy brows'. They are a description of his (fringe, eyebrows, an item of clothing).

Answer these questions.

4 What piece of evidence in the passage suggests that Mrs Mellon had been housekeeper for the Earl for many years?

_____

_____

5 Why was it a 'great day' (line 8)?

_____

_____

6 Explain why when speaking to Mrs Mellon, Mr Havisham did so 'in a low voice' (line 14).

_____

_____

7 Explain in your own words what is meant by the sentence 'But he had attracted attention in one quarter at least' (line 26).

_____

_____

8–9 Find two pieces of evidence that suggest this passage was written many years ago.

_____

_____

_____

10 Why do you think the Earl 'scarcely knew what to say' (line 42) on meeting Little Lord Fauntleroy?

_____

_____

7

D 6

Underline the correct form of the **verb** to complete each sentence.

11 The dogs race/races after the ball.

12 Ben stir/stirs the cake mixture.

13 The chick learns to scratch/scratches the earth.

14 The Head Teacher sing/sings loudly and clearly during assembly.

15 The rain pour/pours down on the washing hung on the line.

16 Rashid peel/peels a banana.

17 The duck feed/feeds greedily on the bread.

7

Extend each of these words into a different **compound word**.

18 table_____

19 table_____

20 any_____

21 any_____

22 snow_____

23 snow_____

24 hand_____

25 hand_____

26 some_____

27 some_____

Add a different **adjective** in each gap to complete the sentences.

28 All the children liked the _____ classroom.

29 The _____ spoon was used for cake-making.

30 George didn't like his _____ teacher.

31 The _____ chickens scratched in the vegetable garden.

32 Eva's _____ computer made researching her homework much easier.

33 The Asser family excitedly headed towards the _____ circus.

Write a word to match each clue. Each word ends in a vowel.

34 A small wind instrument _____

35 A mountain with a crater _____

36 A folding frame covered with fabric which opens to give

protection _____

37 A liquid for washing hair _____

38 Tiny pieces of coloured paper, often thrown over newlyweds _____

39 A flat round of dough covered with a savoury mixture _____

40–45 Write an account of a car accident. Include an adverbial of time, an adverbial of place, two question marks and two exclamation marks.

D 1

D 5

_____

_____

_____

_____

_____

_____

6

With a line, match the words with the same key spelling patterns.

E 2

46	experience	balance
47	thorough	agent
48	performance	optician
49	plumber	borough
50	entrant	licence
51	present	instant
52	electrician	numbness

7

Write whether each of these sentences is in the **past**, **present** or **future tense**.

D 6

53 I walked home. _____

54 I am going to buy lunch. _____

55 I wrote an exciting story. _____

56 I am sipping my soup carefully. _____

57 I have made some cakes. _____

58 I will tidy my bedroom. _____

59 I am typing at my computer. _____

7

21

Write each of these words adding the **suffix** *ful* correctly.

60 thought _____

61 awe _____

62 pity _____

63 deceit _____

64 shame _____

65 mercy _____

66 hope _____

67 dread _____

E 2
8
D 2

Complete each sentence by adding a different **conjunction**.

68 I still went swimming _____ I had a bad cold.

69 Laurel chose to go to Horseworld for her birthday treat _____ she loves horses.

70 Mum bought me some new trainers _____ I could run faster!

71 Niall wanted to go out on his bike _____ it was raining.

72 Wusai missed a day off school _____ so did Gina.

73 Jacob has been able to use a knife and fork _____ he was three.

74 Dan's new puppy couldn't go for a walk _____ he had all his injections.

75 We left the swimming pool _____ it was closing.

8
C 4

Write which animal these **onomatopoeic** words remind you of.

76 roar _____

77 baa _____

78 grunt _____

79 gobble _____

80 mew _____

81 cluck _____

82 woof _____

7
D 6

Underline the **pronouns** in the sentences.

83–84 We must buy him a packet as well.

85–87 Where is mine? Have you got it?

88–89 His is longer than yours.

90 Why are theirs the same?

91–92 I wonder what they are doing.

10

Rewrite these words adding the **suffix** *able* or *ible* to each one.

93 adore _____   94 notice _____

95 collapse _____   96 access _____

97 desire _____   98 reverse _____

99 sense _____   100 move _____

8

Now go to the Progress Chart to record your score!   Total   100

Paper 5

Water in Our World

Three-quarters of Earth's surface is covered by water and
nearly all of it is contained in the oceans and seas.
The rest, a very small amount, is in the air or froze long ago
to form polar ice caps. Most of the water we use comes from
rivers and lakes, or water that has seeped through rocks and collected underground.   5

● The movement of water between the land, the sea and the air is called the water
cycle. As the Sun heats the water in the oceans, rivers, lakes and plants, some of
the water evaporates, which means that it changes into water vapour (a gas) and
rises into the air. High in the sky, the water vapour cools and changes back into tiny
drops of liquid water. This process is called condensation. The water drops   10
gather together to make clouds and eventually fall as rain, hail or snow. The cycle
then starts all over again. As a result of this recycling, the amount of water on Earth
always remains the same.

● About 97 per cent of all water is the salty water of the oceans and seas. The sea is
salty because salts are either washed off the land by rivers or escape from   15
cracks in the ocean floor. Other salts come from undersea volcanoes.

● Water makes up the greatest part of the bodies of plants and animals and is vital
for all life. Did you know that your body is made up of more than 70 per cent water?
You need to take in about two litres of water a day, and much more when it is hot or
you are working hard. Aquatic animals live surrounded by water, but those that   20
live on land have to find water or get all that they need from their food.

● Sea water has no colour, but appears blue or green because both blue and
green light from the Sun reach deeper below the surface of the water than
other colours. The sea also reflects the colour of the sky and changes in the
weather.   25

From Questions and Answers: Oceans and Rivers by Barbara Taylor

23

Underline the correct answers.

1 What is the Earth's surface mainly covered in?

(land, water, land and water equally)

2 What percentage of water on Earth is salty?

(3%, 70%, 97%)

3 What colour is sea water?

(blue, green, clear)

Answer these questions.

4 Why is condensation described as a 'recycling' process (line 12)?

_____

_____

_____

_____

5 What does the word 'reflects' mean (line 24)?

_____

_____

6-7 Give two reasons why the sea is salty.

_____

_____

_____

_____

8-9 Read this sentence: *If people don't get enough water from eating and drinking they may become dehydrated.* In which bullet point would this sentence best fit and why?

_____

_____

3

10 Look again at the third bullet point. Write a subheading in the form of a question for this paragraph.

_____

_____

7

D 6

Circle the **preposition** (a word that relates other words to each other) in each of these sentences.

11 Gran slept for hours in the armchair.

12 Jay jumped behind the leather sofa.

13 Caroline walked carefully among the bluebells.

14 Yousef climbed up the cliff wall.

15 The twins looked through the letterbox to see if anyone was home.

16 The electrician slipped down the ladder and broke his leg.

17–18 Mum placed the drinks on the tray before carrying them up the stairs.

8

D 10

Write the short form often used for each of these words.

19 aeroplane _____

20 handkerchief _____

21 head-teacher _____

22 newspaper _____

23 champion _____

24 examination _____

6

D 6

Add _cial_ or _tial_ to complete these words.

25 commer _____

26 par _____

27 confiden _____

28 artifi _____

29 ini _____

30 spe _____

31 finan _____

7

D 9

Write a **synonym** for each of the words in bold.

32 The captured soldiers were **interrogated**. _____

33 Mum complained about the **racket** my music made. _____

25

34 I was surprised that such a famous person looked so **ordinary**.

_____

35 Dave was given the **option** to go ice-skating or to the cinema.

_____

36 The Captain **reviewed** his troops.   _____

37 The rope around their wrists was **taut**.   _____

38 That's **wonderful** news!   _____

7

D 4
D 5

Rewrite these sentences, adding the missing punctuation.

39–42 What time does the party start Helen called

_____

_____

43–49 We must concentrate said David If we don't get this work done we'll have to miss our playtime

_____

_____

11

E 2

Match to each of these words a word with the same letter string but a different sound.

stove   height   barn   head   glove   plead

50 weight   _____   **51** earn   _____

52 love   _____   **53** bead   _____

54 drove   _____   **55** dead   _____

6

D 13

Rewrite these sentences without the double negatives.

56 Jake hasn't walked no half-marathon.

_____

57 There wasn't no milk left by the milkman.

_____

58 Cath hasn't no drink for her lunch.

_____

59 Dad's not never going there again.

_____

60 There aren't no red squirrels here.

_____

61 I don't not have enough money to buy that.

_____

6

Write a **homophone** for each of these words.

E 2

62 site	_____	**63** boarder	_____
64 horse	_____	**65** stationary	_____
66 flower	_____	**67** shore	_____
68 wave	_____	**69** sundae	_____

8

Add a powerful **verb** in the gaps to make each sentence interesting.

D 6

70–71 The dog _____ towards the sea and _____ into it.

72–73 The plane _____ and the passengers _____.

74–75 '_____ or we'll never win the relay race!' _____ the team.

76–77 The children _____ through the snow until they could see the

_____ lights.

78–79 As the queen _____ the crowd _____.

10

27

Put these counties in **alphabetical order**.

Northumberland   Somerset   Suffolk   Norfolk
South Glamorgan   Nottinghamshire   Strathclyde

80 (1) _____   **81** (2) _____

82 (3) _____   **83** (4) _____

84 (5) _____   **85** (6) _____

86 (7) _____

○ 7

Underline the **connectives** (word or words that join clauses or sentences) in each sentence.

87 Ella had to sit down for tea even though her favourite programme was on.

88 Daniel needed his boots but he couldn't find them.

89 The runner had hurt his ankle, nevertheless he still started the race.

90 Veejay handed in his homework although it was past the deadline.

91 The kittens drank their milk and chased the ball before settling down for the night.

92 It was time for Jane to go home though she wanted to stay longer.

○ 6

Circle the words which have a soft 'g'.

93–100 knowledge   gaggle   garage   imagine   gourd   refugee   generous

governor   dungeon   gradient   gigantic   grime   message   wrong   frog

○ 8

Now go to the Progress Chart to record your score!   **Total** ○ 100

When the end of the war did come, it came swiftly, almost unexpectedly it seemed to the men around me. There was little joy, little celebration of victory, only a sense of profound relief that at last it was finished and done with. Albert left the happy cluster of men gathered together in the yard that cold November morning and strolled over to talk to me. 'Five minutes time and it'll be finished, Joey, all over. 5 Jerry's had about enough of it, and so have we. No one really wants to go on any more. At eleven o'clock the guns will stop and then that will be that. Only wish that David could have been here to see it.'

Since David's death Albert had not been himself. I had not once seen him smile or joke, and he often fell into prolonged brooding silences when he was with me. 10 There was no more singing, no more whistling. I tried all that I could to comfort him, resting my head on his shoulder and nickering gently to him, but he seemed quite inconsolable. Even the news that the war was finally ending brought no light back to his eyes. The bell in the clock tower over the gateway rang out eleven times, and the men shook each other solemnly by the hand or clapped each other on the back 15 before returning to the stables.

The fruits of victory were to prove bitter indeed for me, but to begin with the end of the war changed little. The Veterinary Hospital operated as it always had done, and the flow of sick and injured horses seemed rather to increase than to diminish. From the yard gate we saw the unending columns of fighting men marching jauntily 20 back to the railway stations, and we looked on as the tanks and guns and wagons rolled by on their way home. But we were left where we were. Like the other men, Albert was becoming impatient. Like them he wanted only to get home as quickly as possible.

Morning parade took place as usual every morning in the centre of the cobbled 25 yard, followed by Major Martin's inspection of the horses and stables. But one dreary, drizzling morning, with the wet cobbles shining grey in the early morning light, Major Martin did not inspect the stables as usual. Sergeant 'Thunder' stood the men at ease and Major Martin announced the re-embarkation plans for the unit. He was finishing his short speech: 'So we shall be at Victoria Station by six o'clock 30 on Saturday evening – with any luck. Chances are you'll be home by Christmas.'

'Permission to speak, sir?' Sergeant 'Thunder' ventured.

'Carry on, Sergeant.'

'It's about the 'orses, sir,' Sergeant 'Thunder' said. 'I think the men would like to know what's going to 'appen with the 'orses. Will they be with us on the same ship, 35 sir? Or will they be coming along later?'

Major Martin shifted his feet and looked down at his boots. He spoke softly as he did not want to be heard. 'No, Sergeant,' he said. 'I'm afraid the horses won't be coming with us at all.'

From *War Horse* by Michael Morpurgo

Underline the correct answers.

1 In which month did the war end?

(October, November, December)

2 Who is Joey?

(a soldier friend of Albert's, a wounded soldier, a horse)

2

Answer these questions.

3 Why had Albert 'not been himself' (line 9)?

_____

4 What was the significance of the bell at the gateway ringing out eleven times?

_____

_____

5 Write another word the author could have used instead of 'nickering' (line 12).

_____

6–7 Give the meaning of the following words as they are used in the passage:

profound (line 3)   _____

jauntily (line 20)   _____

8–9 Using evidence from the passage, describe how you think war has affected Albert.

_____

_____

_____

_____

10 In lines 37–38 the sergeant 'spoke softly as he did not want to be heard'. Why?

_____

_____

_____

8

D 6

Write the **collective noun** for each of these living creatures.

11 elephants	_____	**12** sheep	_____
13 kittens	_____	**14** ants	_____
15 fish	_____	**16** lions	_____
17 bees	_____	**18** seagulls	_____

8

Write six sentences, each with a relative clause beginning with the following words or an omitted pronoun.

D 2

19 who _____

_____

20 which _____

_____

21 that _____

_____

22 whose _____

_____

23 whom _____

_____

24 omitted pronoun _____

_____

6

Add *ory*, *ery* or *ary* to each of these words.

E 2

25 Febru_____   **26** diction_____   **27** hist_____

28 myst_____   **29** ordin_____   **30** secret_____

31 jewell_____   **32** necess_____   **33** mem_____

9

Add the missing apostrophe or apostrophes to each sentence.

D 5

34 Dont go over there!

35 We couldve gone to the beach.

36 Theyll be home soon.

37–38 Its time to go to ballet, isnt it?

39 I shant eat my tea!

40 Well buy some sweets tomorrow.

7

Complete each of these expressions using the words below.

bush   cart   apple   ghost   head   rat   heart

41 Don't give up the _____.

42 To smell a _____.

43 To hang your _____ in shame.

44 To put the _____ before the horse.

45 Absence makes the _____ grow fonder.

46 Don't beat about the _____.

47 An _____ a day keeps the doctor away.

7

Rewrite these book titles, adding the missing capital letters.

48–50 classic children's stories

_____

51–54 the little book of facts

_____

55–58 keeping ponies season by season

_____

11

D 6

Circle the word which is …

59 a **verb**	bus	happily	bounce	it
60 a **pronoun**	they	ran	through	rain
61 a **noun**	tree	but	pretty	before
62 an **adverb**	gate	new	kicked	greedily
63 a **preposition**	under	marmalade	we	you
64 an **adjective**	jacket	lank	love	swarm
65 a **conjunction**	hidden	giant	cold	although

7

Some questions will be answered in the children's own words. Answers to these questions are given in *italics*. Any answers that seem to be in line with these should be marked correct.

Paper 1

1 a range of mountains
2 a magician
3 me, be, MC, we
4 *parents*, *adults*
5 The words are written in italics.
6–8 *The adults are controlling and haven't really listened to the child who might be feeling put down and dismissed.*
9–10 *The child is confident and believes in him or herself. For example, even after being told by the parents that he or she can't be lots of things, the child continues to believe that he or she can be. This is shown when the child says 'They do not realise I can fulfil any ambition'.*

11 lanterns	12 atlases
13 diseases	14 chocolates
15 calves	16 athletes
17 foxes	18 roofs
19 ran	20 searched
21 read	22 grew
23 went	24 felt
25 .	26 .
27 ! or .	28 ?
29 ! or .	30 ?
31 .	32 *glove*
33 *thorough*	34 *brought*
35 *plough*	36 *dough*
37 *prove*	38 *bellow*
39 *tough*	40 slow
41 hide	42 sip
43 gregarious	44 content
45 accurate	46 endanger

47–54 We regretted leaving our jumpers behind. It had become cold and we could have done with them for protection from the biting wind. Still we battled on against the elements. It was so important we made it before darkness fell.
55 answer
56 ballet
57 honour
58 wriggle
59 solemn
60 rhythm
61 island
62 exhibit
63–64 the two cars' horns
65–66 the five girls' jumpers
67–68 the six birds' beaks
69–70 the four dogs' leads

71 *resourceful*	72 *shapeless*
73 *excitement*	74 *woeful*
75 *remoteness*	76 *falsehood*
77 *tameness*	78 *tunefully*
79 *lovingly*	80 *accidentally*

81 wistfully	82 wearily
83 angrily	84 cheekily

85–86 The team played its best.
87–89 The cinema in the area was showing the latest release.
90–92 The bonfire burnt for an hour.
93–100 February, Bath Rugby Club, Aberdeen, Sydney Harbour, Windsor Castle, Blue Peter, Ben Nevis, Alex Roberts

Paper 2

1 Oliver's
2 he tells lies
3 didn't
4 *Responses from the penpals began to arrive, a few at a time, in class.*
5 *His mother became angry/upset.*
6 *To emphasise the fact that he was really upset and not just pretending.*
7–8 *Simon actually threw the letter in the dustbin. He said that he accidentally lost it because he didn't want to admit that he threw it away.*
9–10 *Simon's argument is not valid and is obviously made up to support the outrageous lie he has told. The lie does show, however, that Simon has a good imagination.*
11–17 herd, cheese, booklet, Richard, antelope, fracture, hate

18 ir	19 non
20 dis	21 im
22 ir	23 im
24 dis	25 dis

26–27 Jess had to feed her cat, give fresh water to the chickens, take the dog for a walk and let the sheep out before school.
28–30 It was wet, blustery, sunny, warm and windy during the Todd family walk.
31–33 Joseph spent his pocket money on a small pot of paint for his model aircraft, a magazine, a card for his mum's birthday, a chocolate bar and a drink.
34–35 *cry*, *snivel*, *weep*
36–37 *calm*, *friendly*, *gentle*
38–39 *huge*, *gigantic*, *massive*
40 Aimee wanted to go horse riding despite the pouring rain.
41 Nazar lost his coat at school on the coldest day of the year.
42 The snow fell heavily for many hours.
43 Dad stopped at the side of the road to answer his phone.
44 Helen ordered a cup of tea and an iced bun from the café on the high street
45 Eleni worked hard at solving her maths problem despite her headache.
46 sub
47 sub
48 tele
49 sub
50 tele
51 sub

52 sub
53 sub
54 *sprint, race*
55 *guffaw, chuckle, giggle*
56 *fling*
57 *gulp*
58 *soaked, drenched*
59 *yell, scream*
60 trans<u>atlan</u>tic
61 <u>idle</u>ness
62 <u>partner</u>ship or part<u>ner</u>ship
63 <u>place</u>ment
64 non-<u>toxic</u>
65 un<u>real</u>
66 <u>danger</u>ously or <u>dangerously</u>
67 <u>assess</u>ment
68 bi<u>cycle</u>
69–70 The apples on their side of the fence are **theirs** but those on our side are **ours**.
71–72 **Yours** is the same as **mine**.
73–74 **His** is bigger than **mine**.
75–76 **His** tasted better than **hers**.

77	planned	78	admitting
79	balloted	80	taxing
81	referred	82	cancelled
83	tested	84	focussing
85	preferred	86	hopping/hoping
87	*Stop*	88	*Hurry*
89	*Run*	90	*Halt*
91	*Shout*	92	*Rattle*
93	*Smile*	94–95	assistant assistance

96–97 tolerant tolerance
98–99 innocent innocence
100 obedient or obedience

Paper 3

1 three hours before
2 it tops up your energy levels
3 because there are many runners wanting to cross the start line
4 *because the race is a distance from the runner's own home*
5–6 to allow plenty of preparation time; to allow for delays getting to the race
7 It isn't easy to stop part way through a race to go to the toilet.
8 sustain – *to keep up one's energy levels*
9–10 to keep warm; they are of no value so can be thrown away once taken off
11 h<u>ei</u>r
12 dec<u>ei</u>ve
13 fr<u>ei</u>ght
14 v<u>ie</u>w
15 conc<u>ei</u>ve
16 y<u>ie</u>ld
17 n<u>ei</u>ghbours
18 s<u>ei</u>ze
19 conc<u>ei</u>ted
20 I enjoy swimming.
21 I made my favourite cakes.
22 I love playing football.

23 The teacher stopped me on the way to class./I stopped her on the way to class.
24 *low*
25 *hot*
26 *under*
27 *illegal*
28 *easy*
29 *stationary, still, immobile*
30 *sold*
31 *give*
32 *shout*
33–37 Five different modal verbs used in the sentences, e.g. *will, might, should, must, can, may.*
38 Fed up because the computer continually broke down, they decided to buy a new one.
39 The sunbathers lay on the beach all afternoon, unaware of how burnt they were becoming.
40–41 The stranger, a well-dressed man, joined the party.
42 In Madagascar the inner skins of leaves are peeled and then stretched out in the tropical sun, which dries and bleaches them.
43 While Henry was swimming at his local pool, the lights suddenly went off.
44 When it was announced that the fancy-dress competition was about to take place, we huddled together to plan our escape.
45 punches
46 buses
47 sausages
48 convoys
49 dresses
50 waltzes
51 tariffs
52 thieves
53–60 <u>Daisy</u>, <u>Daisy</u>,
Give me your <u>answer</u> do,
I'm half crazy
All for the <u>love</u> of you;
It won't be a stylish <u>marriage</u>,
For I can't afford a <u>carriage</u> –
But you'll look sweet
Upon the <u>seat</u>
Of a <u>bicycle</u> made for two!
61–64 'What do we do now?' grumbled Jay through gritted teeth. 'They're bound to sabotage our camp.'
'They can't do anything until it gets dark,' consoled Mimi. 'We'll just have to make sure we stay up all through the night.'
65–68 'I'm frozen,' complained Jay. 'It really is cold and dark,' he sighed. 'Maybe they aren't going to come back tonight.'
Mimi considered Jay's comment. 'But maybe they will!' she replied.
69 glass
70 gladiator
71 gesture
72 globe
73 gold
74 gnat
75 gradient
76 garbage
77–78 boy, buoy

79–80 fare, fair
81–82 knew, new
83–84 sure, shore
85–86 ewe, yew
87–94 Kate's dad called to her to hurry up.
'Hurry up Kate!' called Dad.
Sarah explained to Pete she was going on holiday soon.
'Pete, I'm going on holiday soon,' explained Sarah.
The Singh family yelled to the passing boat that they needed help.
'Help!' yelled the Singh family to the passing boat.
Mum asked her friend if she thought it might rain today.
'Do you think it might rain today?' Mum asked her friend.
95 piglet
96 booklet
97 duckling
98 hillock
99 owlet
100 statuette

Paper 4

1 Cedric
2 was happy
3 eyebrows
4 *When seeing Lord Fauntleroy, Mrs Mellon made reference to his father so she must have known him.*
5 *It was a great day because Lord Fauntleroy was the heir and he had come to live at his estate.*
6 He didn't want Lord Fauntleroy to overhear what he said.
7 Lord Fauntleroy had been acknowledged by the dog, though not immediately by his grandfather.
8–9 The passage talks about many staff like the housekeeper, footman, etc.; reference is made by Mrs Mellon to the nursery upstairs.
10 *He was delighted/excited about meeting his grandchild and was struck by his confidence, which caught him unawares.*
11 race
12 stirs
13 scratch
14 sings
15 pours
16 peels
17 feeds
18–19 *tablecloth, tabletop*
20–21 *anywhere, anytime*
22–23 *snowball, snowman*
24–25 *handbag, handshake*
26–27 *something, someone*
28 *colourful*
29 *wooden*
30 *strict*
31 *naughty*
32 *new*
33 *noisy*
34 piccolo, flute, whistle, **35** volcano
kazoo, oboe
36 umbrella
37 shampoo
38 confetti
39 pizza
40–45 A short passage that includes an adverbial of time, an adverbial of place, two question marks and two exclamation marks.
46 experience – licence
47 thorough – borough
48 performance – balance
49 plumber – numbness
50 entrant – instant
51 present – agent
52 electrician – optician
53 past
54 future
55 past
56 present
57 past
58 future
59 present
60 thoughtful
61 awful
62 pitiful
63 deceitful
64 shameful
65 merciful
66 hopeful
67 dreadful
68 *although*
69 *because*
70 *so*
71 *but*
72 *and*
73 *since*
74 *until*
75 *as*
76 lion
77 sheep
78 pig
79 turkey
80 cat
81 hen
82 dog
83–84 We must buy him a packet as well.
85–87 Where is mine? Have you got it?
88–89 His is longer than yours.
90 Why are theirs the same?
91–92 I wonder what they are doing.
93 adorable
94 noticeable
95 collapsible
96 accessible
97 desirable
98 reversible
99 sensible
100 movable

Paper 5

1 water
2 97%
3 clear
4 *It is described as a recycling process because the same water is changed into something else (water vapour) then back into liquid water again so it is reused.*
5 reflect – *to show an image of something, to mirror*
6–7 salts are washed off the land/salt escapes from cracks in the ocean floor/salts come from undersea volcanoes
8–9 bullet point three: *it fits best here because this section discusses water and its use and effect on humans*
10 *How important for life is water?*
11 in
12 behind
13 among
14 up
15 through
16 down
17–18 on, up
19 plane
20 hanky
21 head
22 paper
23 champ
24 exam
25 commercial

26 partial
27 confidential
28 artificial
29 initial
30 special
31 financial
32 *questioned*
33 *noise*
34 *unexciting*
35 *choice*
36 *inspected*
37 *tight*
38 *great*
39–42 'What time does the party start?' Helen called.
43–49 'We must concentrate,' said David. 'If we don't get this work done we'll have to miss our playtime.'
50 height
51 barn
52 stove
53 head
54 glove
55 plead
56 Jake hasn't walked a half-marathon.
57 There wasn't any milk left by the milkman.
58 Cath hasn't a drink for her lunch./Cath has no drink for her lunch.
59 Dad's not ever going there again/Dad's never going there again.
60 There aren't any red squirrels here/There are no red squirrels here.
61 I don't have enough money to buy that.
62 sight or cite
63 border
64 hoarse
65 stationery
66 flour
67 sure
68 waive
69 Sunday
70–71 *raced, somersaulted*
72–73 *dived, screamed*
74–75 *sprint, yelled*
76–77 *struggled, shining*
78–79 *tripped, gasped*
80 (1) Norfolk
81 (2) Northumberland
82 (3) Nottinghamshire
83 (4) Somerset
84 (5) South Glamorgan
85 (6) Strathclyde
86 (7) Suffolk
87 Ella had to sit down for tea <u>even though</u> her favourite programme was on.
88 Daniel needed his boots <u>but</u> he couldn't find them.
89 The runner had hurt his ankle, <u>nevertheless</u> he still started the race.
90 Veejay handed in his homework <u>although</u> it was past the deadline.
91 The kittens drank their milk and chased the ball <u>before</u> settling down for the night.
92 It was time for Jane to go home <u>though</u> she wanted to stay longer.

93–100 knowledge, garage, imagine, refugee, generous, dungeon, gigantic, message

Paper 6

1 November
2 a horse
3 *Albert had not been himself since David, obviously a close friend or relative, had died.*
4 It was at that moment the end of the war had arrived. It was the eleventh hour of the eleventh month.
5 nickering – *whinnying*
6–7 profound – *deep, intense*
jauntily – *cheerfully*
8–9 *Albert had become sad, quiet and unhappy. This is shown when the author says that he no longer smiled or joked and that even when he knew that the war was ending, there was no light in his eyes.*
10 He knew that his men cared deeply for the horses, as shown in the relationship between Albert and Joey, and he knew this would be bad news for them.
11 herd
12 flock or herd
13 litter
14 colony
15 school or shoal
16 pride
17 swarm
18 flock
19–24 Six sentences, each with a relative clause using the listed words or omitting a pronoun, e.g. That's the girl *who* lives near my uncle.
25 February
26 dictionary
27 history
28 mystery
29 ordinary
30 secretary
31 jewellery
32 necessary
33 memory
34 Don't go over there!
35 We could've gone to the beach.
36 They'll be home soon.
37–38 It's time to go to ballet, isn't it?
39 I shan't eat my tea!
40 We'll buy some sweets tomorrow.
41 ghost
42 rat
43 head
44 cart
45 heart
46 bush
47 apple
48–50 Classic Children's Stories
51–54 The Little Book of Facts
55–58 Keeping Ponies Season by Season
59 bounce
60 they
61 tree
62 greedily
63 under

64 lank
65 although
66 I've been swimming./I went swimming./I was going swimming.
67 The thunder was frightening.
68 The children have picked blackberries./The children were going to pick blackberries./The children went to pick blackberries.
69 My gran lived/was living on her own.
70 The dog swam/was swimming in the pond.
71 The school orchestra has practised/were practising.
72–75 Internet, website, email, DVD
76 ignore
77 annoy
78 reassure
79 reply
80 was
81 are
82 are
83 is
84 was
85 were/was
86–92 innocent, centimetre, electricity, sequence, practice, peace, fancy
93 agreeable
94 direction
95 forceful
96 mismatch
97 optional
98 reloading
99 discoloured
100 tiresome

Paper 7

1 winter
2 to guide her home with a light
3 no
4 *It was just past two in the afternoon and he thought the storm wasn't due for many hours.*
5–6 'She wandered up and down' (line 30); 'And many a hill did Lucy climb' (line 31); 'A furlong from their door' (line 40).
7–8 *They were desperate and upset. This is shown when the poet says that they were 'wretched' and they 'wept'.*
9–10 the language the poem is written in; the fact Lucy was carrying a lantern rather than a torch
11 their
12–13 They're, their
14–15 there, they're
16–17 to, to
18–19 two, too
20 too
21 Freda, the long-haired, cream-coloured cat, slept soundly.
22 Florence loved her thick, long, dark hair.
23 Jim dived through the sticky, wet mud, saving the goal.
24 The friends burnt while playing in the blistering, scorching heat of the sun.
25 The baby-sitter told exciting, but scary and often terrifying, late night stories!
26 The glistening, coloured vase shimmered in the sunlight.
27 skin and blister – sister
28 apples and pears – stairs
29 bread and cheese – knees
30 plates of meat – feet
31 sugar and honey – money
32 frog and toad – road
33 *amusing, funny*

34 *change, alter*
35 *dull, tedious*
36 *hide, conceal*
37 *sway*
38 *pull*
39 *strange*
40 *damage*
41–58 'Listen everyone, I have an announcement to make,' shouted Mr Bridges above the noise. 'I've arranged for us all to camp out at Harlington Hall. We will see for ourselves if it is haunted or not!'
The colour faded from Hannah's face.
59 armies
60 quantities
61 trolleys
62 cowboys
63 novelties
64 responsibilities
65 stairways
66 remedies
67 CID
68 km
69 DIY
70 UN
71 UFO
72 VIP
73 e.g. or eg
74–79 *co-ordinate, re-enter, co-own, cross-country, co-author, co-star, ex-directory*
80 Sarah enquired what time we should meet.
81 A hungry boy exclaimed that it must be lunchtime.
82 Tony moaned he wished he didn't have so much work to do.
83 The park keeper called out that dogs weren't allowed in the park.
84 Mum shouted I should clear up my room.
85 Jane asked whether I had checked out a website.
86 soreness
87 regardless
88 plentiful
89 achievement
90 examination
91 shapeless
92 stressful
93 tiresome
94 *although*
95 *where*
96 *because*
97 *but*
98 *as*
99 *when*
100 *which*

Paper 8

1 600 million
2 money each month to support their work
3–4 *It helps the sponsors give the children and their families things they need such as clean water.*
5 community leaders, parents and the children themselves
6 *An 'income-generating scheme' is one which provides skills and supplies to enable families to support themselves.*
7 *polluted/unclean*
8 *It means that each child is capable of leading a rich and successful life.*
9–10 *by giving examples of the problems; by naming some children who need help; by explaining how people can help*
11 ambitious
12 delicious
13 bumptious
14 scrumptious
15 tenacious
16 suspicious
17 infectious
18 ferocious
19–20 The coat lining felt odd, sort of lumpy, and I thought I could hear a faint squeak coming from inside it.

21 As it came nearer, it slowly took on the form of a boat.

22 A dreaded monster lived in the castle nearby, watching over the townsfolk's every move.

23 Rick and James began to argue, each blaming the other for the broken window.

24 You know what it is like, you try to work but you find yourself staring out the window.

25–26 Sam, who was hungry after playing football, was glad to see his mum making sandwiches.

27 billy-goat

28 hero

29 count

30 gander

31 stag or buck

32 nephew

33–39 quickly, impatiently, hurriedly, excitedly, diligently, undeniably, constantly

40–41 *love, desire*

42–43 *run, sprint*

44–45 *small, tiny*

46–47 *calm, still*

48–49 *dark, dim* or *heavy, weighty*

50 confetti

51 volcano

52 spaghetti

53 shampoo

54 umbrella

55 cello

56–64

	er	**est**	**ish**
large	larger	largest	largish
sweet	sweeter	sweetest	sweetish
cold	colder	coldest	coldish

65 *under*

66 *onto*

67 *over*

68–69 *through, along*

70 *around*

71 *in*

72–75 'It's time we set off on holiday,' called Mum.

76–82 'Where is my coat?' shouted Danny, 'it is too cold to go outside without it.'

83 ballet – France

84 karate – Japan

85 dachshund – Germany

86 bravo – Italy

87 He/she/(person's name) fainted with the pain.

88 He/she/(person's name) eats quickly.

89 He/she/(person's name) fell down the stairs.

90 They/(people's names) love playing computer games.

91 He's/she's/(person's name) walking the dog.

92 They're/(people's names) going to see a film.

93-94 was, were

95 is

96 are

97 were

98-99 is, are

100 are

Paper 9

1 a hillside of loose stones

2 no

3 loose stones

4 He had two helpings of goat.

5 immense – *vast, huge, extensive*

6 *It suggests Edmund doesn't have much time for Eustace and is irritated by him.*

7 *because on closer inspection he realised how treacherous the path was*

8 *because he hadn't read stories with dragons or previously been told about them like most children*

9–10 Child's answer describing their interpretation of how Eustace felt, e.g. scared, terrified, cautious but relieved he hadn't yet been noticed. Eustace felt frightened when he saw the dragon. This is shown in the line 'It froze him dead still where he stood for a second.' [This line occurs when he <u>hears</u> the dragon, <u>before</u> he has seen it.]

11 scarves

12 wolves

13 beliefs

14 handcuffs

15 wives

16 penknives

17 remedies

18 motifs

19 anything

20 nothing

21 nothing

22-23 nothing, anything

24 nothing

25 anything

26 *a bad dream*

27 *a piece of anything left over*

28 *to move slowly*

29 *a short rush of strong wind*

30 *brave*

31 *a carefully thought out idea but not yet proven*

32 *horrible, very unpleasant*

33 were

34 will

35 were

36 was

37 shall

38 were

39 are

40 was

41–45 Each of the listed adverbs used correctly in different sentences. For example, *The team waited anxiously as the ball flew towards the goal*.

46–48 On a bright, warm day we like to go to the park.

49–52 When I play with Jack, my pet dog, I usually get tired before he does.

53–56 Nina bought some pens, pencils, rubbers and a ruler before the first day of school.

57 downs

58 thick

59 black

60 going

61 rough

62 less

63 near

64 excellent

65 separate

66 marvellous

67 bruise

68 category

69 individual

70 twelfth

71 restaurant

72–73 <u>I ran quickly up the street</u> *as* <u>Aunty Sam had arrived</u>.

74–75 <u>Helga put on her boots</u> *because* <u>she loved to splash in puddles</u>.

76–77 <u>Guy walked off in the opposite direction</u> *after* <u>he lost his tennis match to Hussan</u>.

78 *drain*   **79** *tough*

80 *blouse*   **81** *rumble*

82 *relate, ultimatum*   **83** *funnel*

84 *lord, chorus*   **85** *universe, diverge*

86 dramatise   **87** *magnetise or magnify*

88 specialise   **89** economise

90 terrorise   **91** verbalise

92 alienate

93–94 slower, slowest

95–96 less, least

97–98 farther/further, farthest/furthest

99–100 larger, largest

Paper 10

1 Helios

2 let the horses guide him

3 was hit by a thunderbolt

4 *Phaeton was keen to show those on Earth that he was the son of a god; to impress his friends.*

5–6 *He thinks about himself but not others. This is shown when he ignores his father's warning and steers the chariot towards Earth just because he wants everyone to see him.*

7 'Light began to climb into the dark sky and the restless horses leaped into the waiting blackness'; 'the wheels and the hooves made splinters of light which surrounded the chariot like a ball of fire'; 'He looked over the side and thought of the people woken by rays from the sun chariot'; the various lines in which the horses send fire to Earth.

8 barren – *unproductive, with few plants or animals*

9 *burnt*

10 *It is always worth listening to, and being prepared to heed, the advice of those who are more experienced than oneself.*

11 overact or react   **12** miscount or recount

13 discharge or recharge   **14** overbalance

15 misbehave   **16** retouch

17 retrace   **18** disbelieve

19 Ben's football had a puncture.

20 They were thirsty, but the cows' water trough was empty.

21 It suddenly rained and the three girls' coats were soaked.

22 Mark's finger hurt after shutting it in a car door!

23 Aunty Sue's family waved as they turned the corner.

24 Dan lost his ticket for football's greatest match, the Cup Final.

25 Five groups' designs were displayed in the school hall.

26–31 wall, London, yellow, diamond, month, egg

32 The teacher called out that we/they should not forget that we/they had homework tonight.

33 The tourist asked where the nearest toilet was.

34 The boy screamed that he was caught in the barbed wire.

35 Greg shouted to stop the ball as it was heading for the goal.

36 Seeta mumbled to her best friend that she really didn't like Mondays.

37–48

noun	pronoun	preposition
chickens	they	for
night	their	to
tonight	he	from
pen	them	into
Jordan	it	
potato		
meal		
home		

49 ✗ [cross symbol]   **50** ✓ [tick symbol]

51 ✓   **52** ✗

53 ✗   **54** ✓

55 ✗   **56** ✓

57–71 Sasha's eyes stared in disbelief. Standing quietly in a stable was her very own pony. 'I don't believe he's mine,' she whispered. Her mother smiled because she knew Sasha deserved him.

72 OAP   **73** cm

74 GB   **75** HQ

76 PM   **77** WC

78–83 Adjectival phrases added to the gaps in the sentences, e.g. *Tom washed his hands in the* <u>warm and soapy</u> *water.*

84–86 *crash, clap, bang*

87–89 *clickety-clack, whoosh, chug-chug*

90–92 *splash, scream, gasp*

93 hiding   **94** equipping

95 picnicking   **96** amusing

97 testing   **98** enrolling

99 thieving   **100** separating

Paper 11

1 American   **2** 1968

3 the passage doesn't specify

4 The achievement of making it to the North Pole first.

5 'on top of the Earth'

6 *only fellow explorers are really aware of who he is and what he has achieved*

7–10 *he is described as the 'explorers' explorer'; the journey to the North Pole was just one expedition he led; he mapped about 45,000 square miles of the pole and personally drew maps which explorers still use today; he was knighted (Sir Wally)*

11–12 *meantime, meanwhile*

13–14 *overdone, overtake, overboard, overnight, overhead, overgrown*

15–16 *weekend, weekday*

17–18 *firewood, fireguard, fireman, firework, fireplace*

19–21 Three sentences each including the listed preposition, e.g. *The cat sat **under** the tree and watched the bird*; *I placed the mug **in** the cupboard when it was dry*; *We walked **along** the shore and listened to the sea.*

22–24 Three of the child's chosen prepositions, such as: *behind*, *near*, *up*, *through*, *over*, *before*, *on*, *below*

25–34 Having emptied the larder, Uncle Franklin returned to the rocking chair. He belched loudly, then grinned, trying to make a joke out of it.

Mum walked in, in time to hear the burp. 'Please Frank, don't do that!' she exclaimed. 'Isn't it time you were heading home?'

'I've missed the train,' he explained, 'thought I'd stay longer.'

35 *language, terms*
36 *period, time*
37 *convince*
38 *disruption, disturbance*
39 *dived, jumped*
40 *took*
41 *pushed*
42 *programme, show*
43 *as, because, for*
44 *although, but, however*
45 *until*
46 *although, but, however*
47 *so, therefore*
48 *and, so, therefore, while*
49 There were no parking spaces/There weren't any parking spaces.
50 I wasn't going to the park/I was not going to the park.
51 We have no money for the fair rides/We haven't any money for the fair rides.
52 There is no chance we'll make it for the start of the match/There isn't a/any chance we'll make it for the start of the match.
53 Jim hasn't bought a new coat.
54 safe   55 scarf
56 trousers   57 hero
58 sheep   59 crocus
60 berry   61 shelf
62–63 were, was
64–65 was, was
66–67 were, were
68–69 were, was
70 tastier   71 playful
72 easily   73 employed
74 spying   75 buyer
76 beautiful   77 merriment
78 future   79 past
80 present   81 present
82 future   83 present
84 past   85 past
86–91

France	Germany	Italy
croissant	schnitzel	studio
boutique	fahrenheit	ravioli

92 frighten
93 signify   94 solidify
95 fossilise   96 glorify
97 apologise   98 has
99 did   100 are

Paper 12

1 between a lake and a forest
2 old   3 fretful
4–6 Linden wood (limewood); moss and rushes; reindeer sinews
7–8 *Native American. The poem uses the word 'wigwam' which is a Native American cone-shaped dwelling.*
9–10 *It was important so he could grow up watching out for dangers but also to understand the ways of his people.*
11 rhinoceros   12 buffet
13 scratch   14 raspberry
15 biscuit   16 wristwatch
17 heiress   18 sword
19–24 Three sentences, one with brackets, one with commas and one with dashes to indicate parenthesis.
25–40

Proper nouns	Abstract nouns	Common nouns	Collective nouns
Bath Rugby Club	jealousy	desk	colony
Iraq	dislike	holiday	gaggle
Keswick	beauty	microscope	flock
Charlie	love	puppy	bunch

41 *splash, splat*   42 *vroom*
43 *squelch*   44 *crackle*
45 *crash, bang*   46 they've
47 there'll   48 wouldn't
49 shan't   50 it's
51 I'll   52 could've
53 doesn't
54 Monty the dog slept soundly (*as, because*) he was exhausted after his walk.
55 Tariq received his swimming certificate (*as, after, because*) he swam 30 lengths of the pool.
56 Sophie was very excited (*as, because, when*) she was having a sleepover at Helen's house.
57 Dan dropped the books he was holding (*after, as, because, when*) Meena gave him a fright.
58 impatient   59 unpleasant
60 illiterate   61 uninterested
62 illegible   63 unreliable
64 impossible   65 illogical
66–86 'What are we going to do?' I wailed. 'We are really going to be in trouble this time.'
'Only if they catch us,' replied Finn.
'But they are bound to,' I mumbled.
87–88 *cloudy, heavy*
89–90 *you, she*
91–92 *behind, over*
93–94 *as, because*
95 thought   96 assist
97 possess   98 assemble
99 help   100 compute

Rewrite these sentences in the **past tense**.

66 I'm going swimming.

_____

67 The thunder is frightening.

_____

68 The children are going to pick blackberries.

_____

69 My gran is living on her own.

_____

70 The dog is swimming in the pond.

_____

71 The school orchestra are practising.

_____

6

Underline the four words or terms that have entered our language in the last fifty years.

E 2

72–75 Internet   website   automobile   television   email   electricity   telephone   DVD

4

Underline one word in each group which is not a **synonym** for the rest.

D 9

76 respond	acknowledge	ignore	answer	reply
77 charm	cheer	amuse	annoy	delight
78 reassure	worry	agonise	upset	unsettle
79 ask	investigate	quiz	examine	reply

4

Finish each sentence by adding a helper **verb** to match the **tense** in bold.

D 6

80 The horse _____ racing towards the sea.   **past**

81 The pigs _____ guzzling down their swill.   **present**

82 The jewels _____ discovered by the thieves.   **present**

83 James _____ running in the relay race.   **present**

84 The telephone _____ ringing.   **past**

85 Fern's class _____ going to read to the younger children.   **past**

6

Circle the words which have a soft 'c'.

86–92 innocent   centimetre   collapse   electricity   catch   sequence

        clueless   ache   practice   synchronise   fantastic   peace

        condense   fancy   alcove

Underline the **root word** of each of these words.

93 agreeable		**94** direction		**95** forceful	
96 mismatch		**97** optional		**98** reloading	
99 discoloured		**100** tiresome			

Now go to the Progress Chart to record your score!   Total   100

Paper 7

Lucy Gray; or, Solitude

Oft I had heard of Lucy Gray:
And, when I crossed the wild,
I chanced to see at break of day
The solitary child.

No mate, no comrade Lucy knew;
She dwelt on a wide moor,
– The sweetest thing that ever grew
Beside a human door!   5

You yet may spy the fawn at play,
The hare upon the green;   10
But the sweet face of Lucy Gray
Will never more be seen.

'To-night will be a stormy night –
You to the town must go;
And take a lantern, Child, to light   15
Your mother through the snow.'

'That, Father! will I gladly do:
'Tis scarcely afternoon –
The minster-clock has just struck two,
And yonder is the moon!'   20

At this the Father raised his hook,
And snapped a faggot-band;
He plied his work; – and Lucy took
The lantern in her hand.

Not blither is the mountain roe: 25
With many a wanton stroke
Her feet disperse the powdery snow,
That rises up like smoke.

The storm came on before its time:
She wandered up and down;   30
And many a hill did Lucy climb:
But never reached the town.

The wretched parents all that night
Went shouting far and wide;
But there was neither sound nor sight   35
To serve them for a guide.

At day-break on a hill they stood
They overlooked the moor;
And thence they saw the bridge of wood,
A furlong from their door.   40

They wept – and, turning homeward, cried,
'In heaven we all shall meet;'
– When in the snow the mother spied
The print of Lucy's feet.

Then downwards from the steep hill's edge   *45*
They tracked the footmarks small;
And through the broken hawthorn hedge,
And by the long-stone wall;

And then an open field they crossed:
The marks were still the same;   *50*
They tracked them on, nor ever lost;
And to the bridge they came.

They followed from the snowy bank
Those footmarks, one by one,
Into the middle of the plank;   *55*
And further there were none!

– Yet some maintain that to this day
She is a living child;
That you may see sweet Lucy Gray
Upon the lonesome wild.   *60*

O'er rough and smooth she trips along,
And never looks behind;
And sings a solitary song
That whistles in the wind.

William Wordsworth

Underline the correct answers.

1 In which season was this poem set?

(summer, autumn, winter)

2 Why was Lucy sent to meet her mother?

(to guide her home with a light, to keep her company on her walk home, to ask her to buy a light before the storm)

3 Did Lucy make it to town before the storm?

(yes, no)

Answer these questions.

4 Why did Lucy's father feel it was safe to send her to town?

_____

_____

5–6 Find two lines in the poem that show Lucy had walked a long way.

_____

_____

_____

7–8 How do you think Lucy's parents felt once they discovered she was missing? Use evidence from the poem to support your answer.

_____

_____

_____

_____

9–10 What evidence is there that this poem was written a long time ago?

_____

_____

_____

7

E 2

Write *there*, *their* or *they're* in each of the gaps.

11 The Jacob family were on _____ way home.

12–13 _____ all very tired after _____ late night.

14–15 The chocolate biscuits are _____ but remember _____ for everyone!

5

E 2

Write *to*, *too* or *two* in each of the gaps.

16–17 Dad had _____ walk _____ the station this morning.

18–19 Dave has had _____ days off school and he is not _____ well again today.

20 Mum is going to buy some dog food but I need to remind her she needs some cat food _____.

5

D 2

Underline the **adjectival phrase** in each sentence.

21 Freda, the long-haired, cream-coloured cat, slept soundly.

22 Florence loved her thick, long, dark hair.

23 Jim dived through the sticky, wet mud, saving the goal.

24 The friends burnt while playing in the blistering, scorching heat of the sun.

25 The baby-sitter told exciting, but scary and often terrifying, late night stories!

26 The glistening, coloured vase shimmered in the sunlight.

6

With a line, match the rhyming slang phrases with their meaning.

27 skin and blister		feet
28 apples and pears		knees
29 bread and cheese		sister
30 plates of meat		road
31 sugar and honey		stairs
32 frog and toad		money

6

D 9

Write a **synonym** for each of these words.

33 humorous _____   **34** modify _____

35 monotonous _____   **36** camouflage _____

37 stagger _____   **38** wrench _____

39 unfamiliar _____   **40** vandalise _____

8

Copy the passage, adding the missing capital letters and punctuation.

D 1

D 6

D 5

41–58 listen everyone I have an announcement to make shouted mr bridges above the noise

ive arranged for us all to camp out at harlington hall we will see for ourselves if it is haunted or not

the colour faded from Hannahs face

_____

_____

_____

_____

_____

_____

_____

18

Write each of these words in its **plural form**.

59 army _____

60 quantity _____

61 trolley _____

62 cowboy _____

63 novelty _____

64 responsibility _____

65 stairway _____

66 remedy _____

Write the **abbreviations** of these words.

67 Criminal Investigation Department _____

68 kilometres _____

69 do it yourself _____

70 United Nations _____

71 unidentified flying object _____

72 very important person _____

73 for example _____

74–79 Write six prefixed words that use a hyphen, for example co-operate.

_____   _____

_____   _____

_____   _____

Rewrite these sentences as **reported speech**.

80 Sarah enquired, 'What time shall we meet?'

_____

81 'It must be lunchtime!' exclaimed a hungry boy.

_____

82 'I wish I didn't have so much work to do,' Tony moaned.

_____

83 The park keeper called out, 'Dogs aren't allowed in this park!'

_____

84 'Clear up your room!' shouted Mum.

_____

85 Jane asked, 'Have you checked out this website?'

_____

6

E 2

Add the **suffix** to each of these words. Don't forget spelling changes.

86 sore + ness = _____   **87** regard + less = _____

88 plenty + ful = _____   **89** achieve + ment = _____

90 examine + tion = _____   **91** shape + less = _____

92 stress + ful = _____   **93** tire + some = _____

8

D 2

In each gap add a different **connective**.

94 The soldiers continued to fight _____ they were exhausted.

95 The children finally arrived at the campsite _____ they could set up their tents.

96 George telephoned his Grandad _____ he'd heard he wasn't well.

97 Wang Ling wanted to go out to play _____ she had to finish her story first.

98 Mark was pleased it was football practice _____ it was his favourite sport.

99 Class 6 were cooking _____ they heard the fire alarm.

100 Gaby lost the trainers _____ were the most comfortable to wear.

7

Now go to the Progress Chart to record your score!   **Total**   100

Thinking of sponsoring a child?

Read how for just a small monthly amount you can help bring health and opportunities to children in poor communities.

Every child has potential

There are 600 million children who live on less than 70p a day – that's ten times   5
the UK population.

In Africa, Latin America and large areas of Asia, acute poverty is depriving children of good health. Many children are suffering from avoidable infections or diseases spread through contaminated water.

Trung wants to read An education would be the best start Trung could have in life.   10
But the nearest school is 20 miles away.

Mamadou's family needs seeds Mamadou and his family have a field that could provide food for them but they need seeds, plus advice to help them work their land more effectively.

Amina needs clean water Amina's village only has access to dirty water, so many   15
children's lives are threatened by waterborne illnesses such as dysentery and diarrhoea.

As a sponsor, you can help more children realise that potential

When we begin working with a community, the first thing we do is talk to community leaders, parents and the children themselves to find out what they need most.

It could be access to clean water, a school for both boys and girls, a medical centre   20
or an income-generating scheme so that families can earn a living.

Children represent the future and we believe sponsorship is the best way to help communities. It is children like Trung, Mamadou and Amina who will be able to pass on their knowledge and skills to the next generation.

Taken from a Plan leaflet on sponsoring a child

Underline the correct answers.

1   How many children live on less than 70p a day?

(1 million, 10 million, 600 million)

2   What is this leaflet asking for?

(teachers to help educate children, people to talk with village leaders, money each month to support their work)

Answer these questions.

3–4 How does the money provided by the sponsors help the children who need it? Give one example.

_____

_____

_____

5 Who do the charity workers talk to when they first identify a community that needs help?

_____

_____

6 What is meant by 'an income-generating scheme' (line 21)?

_____

_____

7 What is the meaning of the word 'contaminated' on line 9?

_____

8 What is meant by the heading 'Every child has potential' (line 4)?

_____

_____

9–10 Describe two ways the information presented in the leaflet is used to encourage people to become sponsors.

_____

_____

_____

_____

8

42

Add *cious* or *tious* to complete each of these words.

11 ambi _____   12 deli _____

13 bump _____   14 scrump _____

15 tena _____   16 suspi _____

17 infec _____   18 fero _____

8

D 4

Add the missing commas to these sentences.

19–20 The coat lining felt odd sort of lumpy and I thought I could hear a faint squeak coming from inside it.

21 As it came nearer it slowly took on the form of a boat.

22 A dreaded monster lived in the castle nearby watching over the townsfolk's every move.

23 Rick and James began to argue each blaming the other for the broken window.

24 You know what it is like you try to work but you find yourself staring out the window.

25–26 Sam who was hungry after playing football was glad to see his mum making sandwiches.

8

D 8

Write the masculine form of each of these words.

27 nanny-goat _____   28 heroine _____

29 countess _____   30 goose _____

31 doe _____   32 niece _____

6

D 6

Underline the **adverbs** in the following passage.

33–39 Henry rushed quickly home after finishing school. He waited impatiently as his mum hurriedly finished her phone conversation.
'Mum, Mum, I've been chosen to narrate the school play,' he said excitedly.
'Mrs Smith says I must work diligently at learning the lines so they can start rehearsals as soon as possible.'
'Well done! I always knew you'd get a part in the play but narrator is undeniably a hard role. You'll have to read through the lines constantly so you know them inside out,' said Mum.

7

Write two **antonyms** for each word.

D 9

40–41 hate   _____   _____

42–43 walk   _____   _____

44–45 huge   _____   _____

46–47 windy   _____   _____

10

48–49 light   _____   _____

E 2

Add the missing vowels to each of these words.

50 c__nf__tt__   **51** v__lc__n__   **52** sp__gh__tt__

53 sh__mp__ __   **54** umbr__ll__   **55** c__ll__

6

E 2

Complete the table below.

56–64

	er	est	ish
large			
sweet			
cold			

9

D 6

Write a different **preposition** in each gap.

65 Leo hid _____ his bedding.

66 Poppy climbed _____ the hay bales.

67 The sheepdog jumped _____ the gate.

68–69 The train went _____ the tunnel then _____ the sea wall.

70 The teacher walked _____ the playground.

71 Dev snuggled _____ his duvet to keep warm.

7

Rewrite these sentences and add the missing punctuation.

D 4
D 5

72–75 It's time we set off on holiday called Mum

_____

76–82 Where is my coat shouted Danny it is too cold to go outside without it

_____

_____

11

E 2

With a line, match the word to the country from where you think it is borrowed.

83 ballet	Germany	
84 karate	France	
85 dachshund	Japan	
86 bravo	Italy	

4

D 6

Rewrite each sentence as though you are writing about someone else.

87 I fainted with the pain. _____

88 I eat quickly. _____

89 I fell down the stairs. _____

90 We love playing computer games.

_____

91 I'm walking the dog. _____

92 We're going to see a film.

_____

6

D 6

Underline the correct word in brackets.

93–94 It (was, were) time to go to bed but they (was, were) not tired.

95 What (is, are) Dad going to do about the broken door?

96 When (is, are) the spring bulbs going to appear?

97 The phone rang when we (was, were) outside.

98–99 The volcano (is, are) erupting as the villagers (is, are) sleeping.

100 When (is, are) we going swimming?

8

'At last!' said Eustace as he came slithering down a slide of loose stones (*scree*, they call it) and found himself on the level. 'And now, where are those trees? There *is* something dark ahead. Why, I do believe the fog is clearing.'

It was. The light increased every moment and made him blink. The fog lifted. He was utterly in an unknown valley and the sea was nowhere in sight.   5

At that very moment the others were washing their hands and faces in the river and generally getting ready for dinner and a rest. The work had gone well so far and it was a merry meal. Only after the second helping of goat did Edmund say, 'Where's that blighter Eustace?'

Meanwhile Eustace stared round the unknown valley. It was so narrow and deep,   10 and the precipices which surrounded it so sheer, that it was like a huge pit or trench.

Eustace realised of course that in the fog he had come down the wrong side of the ridge, so he turned at once to see about getting back. But as soon as he had looked he shuddered. Apparently he had by amazing luck found the only possible way down – a long green spit of land, horribly steep and narrow, with precipices on   15 either side. There was no other possible way of getting back. But could he do it, now that he saw what it was really like? His head swam at the very thought of it. He turned round again, thinking that at any rate he'd better have a good drink from the pool first. But as soon as he had turned and before he had taken a step forward into the valley he heard a noise behind him. It was only a small noise but it sounded   20 loud in that immense silence. It froze him dead still where he stood for a second. Then he slewed round his head and looked.

At the bottom of the cliff a little on his left hand was a low, dark hole – the entrance to a cave perhaps. And out of this two thin wisps of smoke were coming. And the loose stones just beneath the dark hollow were moving (that was the noise he had   25 heard) just as if something were crawling in the dark behind them.

Something *was* crawling. Worse still, something was coming out. Edmund or Lucy or you would have recognised it at once, but Eustace had read none of the right books. The thing that came out of the cave was something he had never even imagined – a long lead-coloured snout, dull red eyes, no feathers or fur, a long lithe   30 body that trailed on the ground, legs whose elbows went up higher than its back like a spider's, cruel claws, bat's wings that made a rasping noise on the stones, yards of tail. And the two lines of smoke were coming from its two nostrils. He never said the word *Dragon* to himself. Nor would it have made things any better if he had. But perhaps if he had known something about dragons he would have been   35 a little surprised at this dragon's behaviour. It did not sit up and clap its wings, nor did it shoot out a stream of flame from its mouth. The smoke from its nostrils was like the smoke of a fire that will not last much longer. Nor did it seem to have noticed Eustace.

From *The Chronicles of Narnia: Voyage of the Dawn Treader* by C S Lewis

Underline the correct answers.

1 What is 'scree'?

(a hillside of loose stones, a level area, another word for 'fog')

2 Was Eustace missed by the group immediately?

(yes, no)

3 What was the noise Eustace had heard?

(a fire crackling, his beating heart, loose stones)

Answer these questions.

4 How do we know that Edmund was hungry?

_____

_____

5 What is the meaning of the word 'immense' on line 21?

_____

6 What does the line 'Where's that blighter Eustace?' (lines 8–9) suggest Edmund's relationship with Eustace is like?

_____

_____

7 Why did Eustace hesitate about returning back up the ridge?

_____

_____

8 Why did Eustace not recognise the strange 'thing' as a dragon?

_____

_____

9–10 Describe in your own words how Eustace felt on seeing the dragon and why. Use evidence from the passage to support your answer.

_____

_____

_____

_____

Write each of these words in their **plural** form.

11 scarf _____   12 wolf _____

13 belief _____   14 handcuff _____

15 wife _____   16 penknife _____

17 remedy _____   18 motif _____

8

Add *anything* or *nothing* to each of these sentences.

19 Brian was bored, he couldn't find _____ to watch.

20 'There is _____ to eat,' moaned Tracey.

21 The bag had _____ in it.

22–23 The twins called 'There is _____ to do, we can't find _____ to play with.'

24 Orin said the mess was _____ to do with him.

25 'I'll read _____ to fill the time,' said Kate.

7

Write a **definition** for each of these words.

26 nightmare _____

27 remnant _____

28 dawdle _____

29 gust _____

30 valiant _____

31 theory _____

32 ghastly _____

7

Underline the correct word in brackets.

D 6

33 The Gallop family (was, were) having a day out.

34 Nasar (have, will) pack his bag.

35 Hannah and David (will, were) planning to have a sleepover.

36 Ben left in a hurry but (was, were) there just in time.

37 We (have, shall) climb the apple tree when we get home.

38 They (will, were) going on holiday.

39 The girls (are, was) leaning against the shop window.

40 After the water fight Hugh (was, were) soaking.

8

Write each of these **adverbs** in a sentence.

D 6

41 anxiously

_____

42 fully

_____

43 soon

_____

44 wearily

_____

45 somewhere

_____

5

Copy these sentences and add the missing punctuation and capital letters.

D 1
D 4
D 5

46–48 on a bright warm day we like to go to the park

_____

_____

49–52 when I play with Jack my pet dog I usually get tired before he does

_____

_____

_____

53–56 nina bought some pens pencils rubbers and a ruler before the first day of school

_____

_____

11

D 9

Complete each expression with an **antonym**.

57 ups and _____

58 through _____ and thin

59 _____ and white

60 coming and _____

61 take the _____ with the smooth

62 more or _____

63 _____ and far

7

E 2

Spell each of these words correctly.

64 exselent	_____	**65** seperate	_____
66 marvelous	_____	**67** briuse	_____
68 categry	_____	**69** indivdual	_____
70 twelth	_____	**71** resturant	_____

8

D 2

Underline the two **clauses** in each sentence.

72–73 I ran quickly up the street as Aunty Sam had arrived.

74–75 Helga put on her boots because she loved to splash in puddles.

76–77 Guy walked off in the opposite direction after he lost his tennis match to Hussan.

6

E 2

Next to each word write another word with the same spelling pattern.

78 strain	_____	**79** rough	_____
80 rouse	_____	**81** stumble	_____
82 ultimate	_____	**83** tunnel	_____
84 chord	_____	**85** diverse	_____

8

Change each of these **nouns** or **adjectives** into a **verb** by adding a **suffix**.

D 6

86 drama   _____

87 magnet   _____

88 special   _____

89 economy   _____

90 terror   _____

91 verbal   _____

92 alien   _____

7

Complete the following **adjectives** of comparison.

D 6

Example: quiet	quieter	quietest
93–94 slow	_____	_____
95–96 little	_____	_____
97–98 far	_____	_____
99–100 large	_____	_____

8

Paper 10

*Phaeton desperately wanted to drive his father's chariot. He begged Helios, the
Greek sun god, to allow him as he wanted to impress his friends on Earth. Phaeton
wanted them to believe he was the son of a god. Helios agreed but there was a
warning …*

'… whatever you do,' he said sternly, 'do not try to guide the horses. They know the
path and, if you do not bother them, they will ride in an arc across the sky, until they
reach the safety of the stables in the West.'

He had time to say no more. The great golden courtyard gates swung open. Light
began to climb into the dark sky and the restless horses leaped into the waiting   5
blackness.

Helios watched as the wheels and the hooves made splinters of light which
surrounded the chariot like a ball of fire.

Phaeton held on tightly to the reins. The chariot thundered into the sky with a speed
that made his cloak stream out behind him. The wind lifted his hair and his breath   10
came in gasps.

Gradually, though, he relaxed and he began to enjoy the power and the swiftness
of his flight. He looked over the side and thought of the people woken by rays from
the sun chariot. He laughed aloud when he thought of the power he had to control
people's lives.   15

'Soon I shall be over my village,' he thought happily, but when he looked over at the
ground below him all he could see were patches of grey, brown and green. He was
too far away even to see his village, let alone his house.

In despair he cried, 'No one will see that it is me driving the chariot.' He gave the
reins an angry tug and steered the great horses away from their path in the   20
sky. Nearer to the Earth they swooped. The stallions gathered speed and hurtled
downwards. Too late, Phaeton remembered his father's warning, and he tried
desperately to stop the furious flight. The horses, sensing that they were no longer
controlled, galloped faster and faster. Their flaming nostrils sent fire licking onto the
earth and sparks flew from their hooves. Flames licked buildings, and crops   25

withered and died in the heat. Huge rivers were sucked into the air and only barren, scorched beds remained.

People were in panic. Dust from the parched ground filled their nostrils. Soil crumbled around them. Where were they to turn for help?

Only the father of the gods, Zeus, could help them. Gathering what little they had *30* to offer as gifts, the villagers streamed to his temple and begged for help. Their pitiful cries soon reached the great god and he looked down with amazement at the devastation. He saw the sun chariot racing in great swirls across the sky, the driver hanging on grimly.

Taking a thunderbolt, Zeus hurled it with great force at the frightened boy. It hit *35* Phaeton and its power sent him spinning out of the chariot. His body twisted in space until it landed, broken, on the Earth.

At a command from Zeus, the horses returned to their proper path. Streaming foam from their bodies made a shimmering haze around them and, as night came, the hidden chariot dissolved into the West and the darkness. *40*

From *The Lonely Boy* by Barrie Wade, Ann Wade and Maggie Moore

Underline the correct answers.

1 (Phaeton, Helios, Zeus) is the name of the sun god.

2 Before Phaeton set off on the chariot, Helios warned him to (hold on tight, let the horses guide him, relax and enjoy the ride).

3 What happened to Phaeton when Zeus discovered what he had done? (he was hit by a thunderbolt, he was asked to stop the chariot, he and the chariot were burnt by flames)

Answer these questions.

4 Why was Phaeton keen to drive the chariot?

_____

5–6 Using evidence from the passage, describe Phaeton's character.

_____

_____

_____

_____

7 Copy one line from the passage that shows that the chariot is a **metaphor** for the sun.

_____

_____

_____

8 What does 'barren' mean (line 26)?

_____

9 Write another word for 'scorched'.

_____

10 Describe in your own words the moral of this Greek legend.

_____

_____

_____

_____

7

E 2

Choose the correct **prefix** to complete each word.

mis   dis   over   re

11 _____act   **12** _____count

13 _____charge   **14** _____balance

15 _____behave   **16** _____touch

17 _____trace   **18** _____believe

8

D 5

Rewrite these sentences, adding the missing apostrophes.

19 Bens football had a puncture.

_____

20 They were thirsty, but the cows water trough was empty.

_____

21 It suddenly rained and the three girls coats were soaked.

_____

22 Marks finger hurt after shutting it in a car door!

_____

23 Aunty Sues family waved as they turned the corner.

_____

24 Dan lost his ticket for footballs greatest match, the Cup Final.

_____

25 Five groups designs were displayed in the school hall.

_____

7

Circle the words that do not have an **antonym**.

D 9

26–31 wall   late   London   deep   top   yellow

        careful   diamond   male   month   egg   stay

6

Rewrite these direct speech sentences into **reported speech**.

D 12

32 'Don't forget that you have homework tonight,' called the teacher.

_____

_____

33 'Where's the nearest toilet?' asked the tourist.

_____

34 'Help, I'm caught in the barbed wire!' screamed the boy.

_____

35 'Stop that ball,' Greg shouted as it was heading for the goal.

_____

_____

36 'I really don't like Mondays,' mumbled Seeta to her best friend.

_____

_____

5

Use words from the passage to complete the table.

37–48 The chickens had been put away for the night. It had been easy tonight as they obediently marched to their broken pen, following Jordan as he sneakily tempted them with soggy mashed potato from the evening meal into their home.

noun	pronoun	preposition

12

Put a *tick* (✓) next to the words spelt correctly and a *cross* (✗) next to those spelt incorrectly.

49 feirce	_____		**50** diesel	_____
51 pier	_____		**52** conciet	_____
53 greivous	_____		**54** perceive	_____
55 viel	_____		**56** foreign	_____

8

Rewrite the following correctly.

57–71 sashas eyes stared in disbelief standing quietly in a stable was her very own pony i dont believe hes mine she whispered her mother smiled because she knew sasha deserved him

_____

_____

_____

_____

_____

_____

15

Write the common **abbreviation** for each of these.

72 old age pensioner _____

73 centimetre _____

74 Great Britain _____

56

75 headquarters   _____

76 Prime Minister   _____

77 water closet   _____

6

D 2

Add an **adjectival phrase** to complete each sentence.

78 Tom washed his hands in the _____
water.

79 Danni kicked her _____ bike.

80 The _____
weather put them off walking.

81 The _____ car broke down
once again.

82 Wusai ate the _____ cake hurriedly.

83 Jeremy awoke disturbed after having a _____
nightmare.

6

C 4

Write down three **onomatopoeic** words that can be associated with these.

84–86 thunder

_____   _____   _____

87–89 train station

_____   _____   _____

90–92 swimming pool

_____   _____   _____

9

E 2

Add the **suffix** *ing* to each of these words.

93 hide   _____   **94** equip   _____

95 picnic   _____   **96** amuse   _____

97 test   _____   **98** enrol   _____

99 thief   _____   **100** separate   _____

8

After 37 years, polar explorer is brought in from the cold

On April 7 1909 the American explorer Robert Peary, nine months into an Arctic expedition, recorded an ecstatic entry in his diary. 'The Pole at last!!! The prize of three centuries, my dream and ambition for 23 years! *Mine* at last …'

It was not, however, his. He was some distance from the geographic north pole   5
and had not just become the first man to walk on top of the Earth.

Sixty years after Peary's disputed expedition, a young Briton named Wally Herbert led a four-man dogsled team to the pole, as part of an ambitious and still-unrepeated expedition to cross the Arctic Ocean on foot. In so doing, they became the rightful holders of the record that Peary had falsely claimed.   10

But while Sir Wally, as he became in 1999, may be one of the greatest explorers Britain has produced, he remains relatively unknown outside his field.

'To those that know, he is the man,' the polar explorer Pen Hadow said. 'He is the explorers' explorer, as Sir Ran Fiennes put it.'

In truth, getting to the pole was no more than an incidental ambition for the   15
explorer. On February 21 1968 his party set out from Point Barrow, Alaska, aiming to make the first ever surface crossing of the Arctic Ocean via the north pole. After 15 months on the ice pack – five of them in darkness – the men arrived in Spitzbergen in northern Norway, completing a journey of 3100 km (1926 miles).

'Ice core samples taken by a member of the party have become the benchmark   20
data for all studies into the impact of global warming on the polar ice caps,' Mr Hadow said. 'And that was just one expedition Sir Wally led. He also mapped something like 45,000 square miles, in three areas of the pole. He personally drew the maps, which are still the maps polar explorers use today.'

Taken from an article in *The Guardian* by Esther Addley

Underline the correct answers.

   1 What nationality was Robert Peary?

      (Norwegian, British, American)

   2 In what year did Wally Herbert lead an expedition to the North Pole?

      (1968, 1969, 1970)

   3 When did Wally Herbert arrive in Norway?

      (in daylight hours, in darkness, the passage doesn't specify)

Answer these questions.

4 Robert Peary wrote '*Mine* at last ...'. What was he referring to?

_____

_____

5 Pick out the phrase from the passage which describes where the North Pole is.

_____

6 What is meant by 'unknown outside his field' on line 12?

_____

_____

7–10 How does the article make it clear that Sir Wally is an explorer worthy of note? Refer to the text in your answer.

_____

_____

_____

_____

7

D 11

Write two **compound words** that begin with these words.

11–12 mean   _____ _____

13–14 over   _____ _____

15–16 week   _____ _____

17–18 fire   _____ _____

8

D 6

Use each of these **prepositions** in a sentence of your own.

19 under

_____

20 in

_____

21 along

_____

22–24 List three more **prepositions**.

D 6
6

_____   _____   _____

Copy the passage, adding the missing capital letters.

D 1
D 6

25–34 having emptied the larder, uncle franklin returned to the rocking chair. he belched loudly, then grinned, trying to make a joke out of it.

mum walked in, in time to hear the burp. 'please frank, don't do that!' she exclaimed. 'isn't it time you were heading home?'

'i've missed the train,' he explained, 'thought i'd stay longer.'

_____

_____

_____

_____

_____

_____

_____

10

Write a **synonym** for each word in bold.

D 9

35 Meena found understanding the computer **jargon** a challenge. _____

36 We are having a **spell** of bad weather. _____

37 I was able to **persuade** my brother to lend me his mp3 player. _____

38 Moving house can be a major **upheaval**. _____

39 The swimmer **plunged** into the pool. _____

40 The head-teacher **seized** his mobile phone. _____

41 Jake **barged** into Henri. _____

42 The radio **broadcast** lasted for three hours. _____

8

Add a different **conjunction** to complete each sentence.

D 2

43 Sam and Tony hesitated at the door _____ they were afraid to enter.

44 Aimee wanted the large bag of sweets _____ she couldn't afford them.

45 Denali had to wait for the doctor _____ he was ready.

46 Jess knows it is recorder practice every Friday _____ she always forgets her recorder.

47 It was raining _____ Mum rushed out to collect the washing.

48 Alice went to Tuhil's house _____ Connor went to Fran's.

6

D 13

Rewrite these sentences without double negatives.

49 There weren't no parking spaces.

_____

50 I wasn't not going to the park.

_____

51 We haven't no money for the fair rides.

_____

52 There isn't no chance we'll make it for the start of the match.

_____

53 Jim hasn't bought no new coat.

_____

5

E 2

Write each of these words in their **singular** form.

54 safes _____   55 scarves _____

56 trousers _____   57 heroes _____

58 sheep _____   59 crocuses _____

60 berries _____   61 shelves _____

8

D 6

Add *was* or *were* in each gap to complete each sentence.

62–63 We _____ waiting for Tony who _____ not ready.

61

64–65 I _____ asked to play the lead role in the play and Sean _____ chosen to play my brother.

66–67 They _____ worried about the match with Forest School as last year they _____ at the top of the league.

68–69 As you _____ late for the film at the cinema I assume it _____ impossible to get tickets?

8

E 2

Add the **suffix** to each of these words.

70 tasty + er _____   **71** play + ful _____

72 easy + ly _____   **73** employ + ed _____

74 spy + ing _____   **75** buy + er _____

76 beauty + ful _____   **77** merry + ment _____

8

D 6

Write whether each of these sentences is in the **past**, **present** or **future** tense.

78 I will be going to Disneyland in the summer.   _____

79 We opened our presents quietly.   _____

80 You're eating an apple.   _____

81 He is leaving the house now.   _____

82 The rain will soak the washing on the line.   _____

83 This number challenge is very hard!   _____

84 The clock stopped at 2.30 am.   _____

85 The wind blew the tree down outside our house.   _____

8

E 2

A number of words we use have been 'borrowed' from other languages. Complete the table below, putting the words under the correct country.

86–91 croissant   studio   schnitzel   ravioli   boutique   fahrenheit

France	Germany	Italy

6

Choose the correct **suffix** to turn each **noun** into a **verb**.

en   ise   ify

92 fright   _____

93 sign   _____

94 solid   _____

95 fossil   _____

96 glory   _____

97 apology   _____

Underline the correct word in brackets.

98 He (has, shall) returned the library book on time so won't receive a fine.

99 Rachel (done, did) the dishes after lunch.

100 They (are, was) expected to begin the competition at noon.

Now go to the Progress Chart to record your score!   Total   100

Paper 12

By the shores of Gitche Gumee,
By the shining Big-Sea-Water,
Stood the wigwam of Nokomis,
Daughter of the Moon, Nokomis.
Dark behind it rose the forest,
Rose the black and gloomy pine-trees,
Rose the firs with cones upon them;
   There the wrinkled, old Nokomis
Nursed the little Hiawatha,
Rocked him in his linden cradle,
Bedded soft in moss and rushes,
Safely bound with reindeer sinews;
Stilled his fretful wail by saying,
'Hush! the Naked Bear will get thee!'
   Many things Nokomis taught him
Of the stars that shine in heaven;
Showed him Ishkoodah, the comet,
Warriors with their plumes and war-clubs,
Flaring far away to northward
   At the door on Summer evenings
Sat the little Hiawatha;
Heard the whispering of the pine-trees,
Heard the lapping of the water,
And he sang the song of children,
Sang the song Nokomis taught him:

An extract from *The Story of Hiawatha* by H W Longfellow

63

Underline the correct answers.

B

1 Where did Nokomis live?

(between a lake and a river, between a river and a forest, between a lake and a forest)

2 Is Nokomis, the daughter of the Moon, a young or old person?

(young, old, poem doesn't state)

2

Answer these questions.

3 What word in the poem means 'agitated'? _____

4–6 What was Hiawatha's cot made of?

_____

_____

_____

_____

7–8 What cultural group do you think this poem is about? Why?

_____

_____

9–10 Nokomis taught Hiawatha many things about the world in which he was growing up. Why do you think that was important?

_____

_____

_____

_____

8

E 2

Each word has a missing silent letter. Rewrite the words correctly.

11 rinocerous _____   **12** buffe _____

13 scrach _____   **14** rasberry _____

15 biscit _____   **16** ristwatch _____

17 eiress _____   **18** sord _____

8

Write three sentences. One sentence must include brackets, one commas and one dashes to indicate **parenthesis**.

D 6

19–20 _____

_____

21–22 _____

_____

23–24 _____

_____

6

D 6

Complete the table below.

25–40 jealousy   Bath Rugby Club   colony   dislike   gaggle   desk
Iraq   flock   holiday   microscope   Keswick   beauty
Charlie   puppy   love   bunch

Proper nouns	Abstract nouns	Common nouns	Collective nouns

16

C 4

Write an **onomatopoeic** word for each of the following.

41 a dripping tap   _____

42 a car passing at speed   _____

43 a spade digging in mud   _____

44 a fire burning   _____

45 thunder   _____

5

Write a **contraction** for each of these pairs of words.

D 5

46 they have _____

47 there will _____

48 would not _____

49 shall not _____

50 it is _____

51 I will _____

52 could have _____

53 does not _____

8

Write each of these pairs of short sentences as one sentence.

D 1

54 Monty the dog slept soundly. He was exhausted after his walk.

_____

55 Tariq received his swimming certificate. He swam 30 lengths of the pool.

_____

56 Sophie was very excited. She was having a sleepover at Helen's house.

_____

57 Dan dropped the books he was holding. Meena gave him a fright.

_____

4

Add the **prefix** *un*, *il* or *im* to each of these words.

E 2

58 _____patient

59 _____pleasant

60 _____literate

61 _____interested

62 _____legible

63 _____reliable

64 _____possible

65 _____logical

8

Rewrite the following correctly.

66–86 what are we going to do? i wailed we are really going to be in trouble this time

only if they catch us replied finn

but they are bound to i mumbled

_____

_____

_____

_____

_____

_____

_____

_____

_____

○ 21

Write two words for each of the following word classes.

87–88 adjective _____ _____

89–90 pronoun _____ _____

91–92 preposition _____ _____

93–94 conjunction _____ _____

○ 8

What is the **root word** in each word?

95 thoughtlessness _____   **96** assistance _____

97 possession _____   **98** assembly _____

99 unhelpful _____   **100** computer _____

○ 6

Now go to the Progress Chart to record your score!   **Total** ○ 100

Progress Chart   English 9–10 years Book 2

Total marks	Paper												Percentage
	1	2	3	4	5	6	7	8	9	10	11	12	
100													100%
90													90%
													85%
80													80%
70													70%
60													60%
50													50%
40													40%
30													30%
20													20%
10													10%
0	1	2	3	4	5	6	7	8	9	10	11	12	0%

Date ▶

When you've finished the book use the Next Step Planner ➡